Pardner Money Stories
Volume II

Deanne Heron

HANSIB

Published by Hansib Publications in 2012
London & Hertfordshire

Hansib Publications Limited
P.O. Box 226, Hertford, Hertfordshire, SG14 3WY, UK

Email: info@hansib-books.com
Website: www.hansib-books.com

A catalogue record for this book is
available from the British Library

ISBN: 978-1-906190-53-8

© Deanne Heron

Designed by
Print Resources, Hertfordshire, UK
Printed in The United Kingdom

DEDICATION

To my daughters Sahara and Rebecca; my grandsons, Ishmail and Amiri; my very large extended family all over the world; my friends and their families who keep me laughing and from whom I draw my inspiration.

ACKNOWLEDGEMENTS

Mr Errol Williamson to whom I'll be forever grateful for not only being instrumental in getting my first story published by *The Jamaica Observer* but who collects and posts the stories to me from Jamaica. To Councillor Whit Stennett and Mr Linford Sweeney for their advice and encouragement and Alicia and Angela Henry who continue to give the opportunity to air my stories on Peace FM 90.1, our local radio station.

INTRODUCTION

Pardner Money Stories Volume II is a further collection of short humorous stories which takes a light hearted look at life within an extended Jamaican family living in Manchester, northern England.

It is written in standard English with Jamaican patois dialogue which is easily understood by non-Jamaican patois speakers. The stories highlight the unique sense of humour of Jamaicans in situations which would not ordinarily be considered amusing, their sayings, expressions, customs and their often unusual take on current events. The stories also capture the culture of the migrants of the fifties and sixties from the West Indies and a way of family life that is slowly dying.

The name of the book comes from the savings club known as 'pardner', 'pardna' or 'paatna', the savings club brought from Jamaica which allowed people to save in an informal way for large items. It is also known in other areas of the Caribbean as 'box-hand' and 'Sou Sou'.'Throwing' your pardner was as much business as socialising because the person who ran the pardner for a small tip, was an important link between people in the community. It was the place where people would often meet and exchange news. The pardner was the connecting thread within the community and has proved to be the connection thread between generations.

The Pardner (Patois Version)

From di devil was a bwoy, di penny dem change han' an' tun ina pound,
'Cos fi pay rent an' buy food di money noh nuff fi goh round.
Lawd dem wuk hard fi t'row one hand, two hand or maybe t'ree,
Fi get di draw fi granny new teet' an' di pickney dem school fee.
Paying di pardner, dat blessed generation connecting t'read,
Was safer than using di money fi prop up di mattress on yu bruk down bed.
Papa marry Mama 'cos him pardner draw meant him could afford di ring.
With no parental backitive or bank account di pardner was di only t'ing.
Tiday di pardner strong like lion, mi hear, just wid a different face,
No more counting money pon di kitchen table 'cos it ina different place.
Di modern pardner come now-a-days in a different disguise,
Of standing orders an' technology cos wi did get sting an' havi get wise,
Seh so much money like butter pon puss mout' fi poor man is too much
    temptation,
Fi hop pon one plane heading fi di sun and tek a permanent vacation.

The Pardner (English Version)

For decades the pennies changed hands and turned into pounds,
Because to pay rent and buy food there was never enough to go around.
They worked hard to throw one hand, two hands or maybe three,
To get the draw for granny's new teeth and the children's school fee.
Paying the pardner, that precious generation connecting thread,
Was safer than using the money to prop up the old mattress of your sunken
    bed.
Papa married Mama because his pardner draw meant he could afford the
    ring.
With no parental support or bank account the pardner was the only thing.
Today the pardner is still going strong I hear, just with a different face,
No more counting money on the kitchen table because it's in a different
    place.
The modern pardner comes now in a completely different guise
Of standing orders and technology because we've been stung and got wise,
That so much money to a poor man can be a great temptation,
To hop on a plane heading for the sun and take a permanent vacation.

CONTENTS

1 Driving Me Mad

Children are a blessing. That is what I think anyway because mine, especially my youngest child, Laura, fondly known as Lolly, keep me young and focussed on what the important things in life really are. They are my guide book to make sense of and safely navigate the 21st century. My children may be the reason for most of my grey hair, but hey... hair dye is cheap.

There are occasions when your children may not feel like they are a blessing. Take the nights for example, when feeling like a zombie from lack of sleep, as babies you held them while they screamed non-stop in the early hours, or the nights when they were late home and didn't phone. These are the nights which perhaps are now distant memories. They are the nights your bare feet developed a lasting bond with the floor as you walked the baby from room to room, upstairs and downstairs, plotting revenge for when you are old, senile and in turn able to give them endless trouble and sleepless nights. Do you remember turning the screaming baby this way and that, shifting them from shoulder to shoulder, cuddling them close, holding them at arms' length, patting and rubbing with what starts off as soothing words and quickly turns to pleading desperation ..."*Please, Baby... go to sleep for Mummy... please.*"

All this of course is after you have fed and burped and changed nappy. You put more clothes on because you think they must be too cold and take clothes off again because you think they must be too hot. Then you check every fold of skin and stitch of clothes, convinced that a pin must be sticking them or an ant biting them, but nothing works. You try laughing like a maniac, pulling tongues and making strange faces, all the things that usually get a smile, chuckle or hysterical screams and kicking of chubby legs. You are reduced to blowing raspberries on their little pot bellies 'til your lips go numb. This stops the crying for a few seconds while the child looks at you as if they think you're off your head and catch their breath to scream again.

I remember one night, at the end of my tether, pleading with my partner, Michael, to do something as my head pounded from the incessant high pitched wail; the cry that only a young baby can do where its tongue vibrates with the quivering treble at the end for effect. This is the cry where you seriously become scared that the neighbours or anyone passing the house will think that you are committing murder.

Michael, who had to be up early for work, had already done his soothing shift, pacing the carpet and had handed her over to me without a word. He had started snoring before his head hit the pillow leaving me wondering how on earth men could do that. I must add though that this was the third night in a row we had gone without sleep.

On hearing my desperate plea, with his eyes closed, Michael, like a limbo dancer, had done a horizontal side-ways slide out of the bed. He felt vaguely in the direction which he had thrown his track suit earlier until I put it near his hand. Then, eyes still closed, he had managed to successfully get the top on, after a couple of attempts, before putting both feet into the same leg of his trousers and falling flat on the floor with a curse as he tried to pull them up. At least that woke him up. On another occasion this might have been comical but exhaustion over rode everything and neither of us were in a laughing mood. With gritted teeth and a face which said he had lost the will to live, Michael put on his trainers and got the baby's all in one coat. I clutched my screaming child to my chest and looked at the yawning, unshaven hobo with the bloodshot eyes suspiciously. I'm sure I just looked like the female version of my partner without the stubble, just wild sticking up hair.

"I'm going to take her for a drive in the car," he yawned in explanation as he noticed my hesitancy. "You know she always falls asleep as soon as you start to drive."

The clock said 3.00am and I felt guilty that I could have, even for the fleeting moment, suspected Michael of contemplating foul play towards our child. With a grateful sigh and enthusiastic nod I handed her over. Still half asleep, Michael had stuffed protesting little arms and legs into the quilted suit, zipped it up snugly and put on her woolly hat. Lying on the bed Lolly looked like a little pink puff ball quivering with anger. This was the first of many midnight drives to get our daughter Laura to sleep. Before Michael had closed the front door, I was asleep.

I don't know what time they came back. The first thing I knew was Michael kissing me goodbye. With a groan, I opened one eye which was assaulted by daylight. My ears met silence, complete and blissful. Still disoriented by exhaustion and sleep, panic welled up in me for a moment.

"Where..?"

"It's ok," Michael answered, patting my shoulder. "Go back to sleep. I've fed her and changed her. She'll probably sleep for a couple of hours. She's exhausted."

I know the feeling, I thought. I looked at Michael and hoped my eyes conveyed my gratitude because I could think of no adequate words as I drifted back into heavenly sleep.

Now, smiling, I was sitting in the passenger seat of the little red Vauxall Corsa which I had just collected from the used-car showroom for my daughter, Lolly. This had led to my moment of reflection.

"Whoo!" Lolly screeched, having had a lot of practice of screeching over the years. She bounced excitedly about in the driver's seat of her 18th birthday present. She had passed her driving test a couple of weeks earlier and had worked most evenings after college and weekends to save her half of the cost of the car. This would ferry her to and fro over the Pennine Hills to university in Nottingham. Although we could have bought her the car, Michael had insisted that she had to save half the money towards it. This, he said, was to teach her responsibility and the value of the things she had. I thought that was a good idea because I had to save for four years after passing my driving test before I could afford my first old banger of a car. By this time I had almost forgotten how to drive and had to book a couple of refresher lessons, to the amusement of my instructor. I was the first pupil he had ever had with a full driving licence and 'L' plates.

Getting insurance for Laura's car had been an eye opener, costing almost half the value of the car but it was worth it to see the look on her face. She had insisted that I take several photographs of her posing inside and outside the car to show her friends on 'Facebook'. Having finished mischievously draping herself backwards over the bonnet, to the amusement of the neighbours, Lolly did a screaming lap of honour around the car, like a footballer who had just scored a goal, shouting "Yes! Yes!" before jumping into the driving seat.

Lolly had passed her driving test first time but I had seen her drive so I had already strapped myself into my seat and checked several times that my seatbelt was secure and that it definitely said the car was fitted with air bags. I was taking her out for her first journey on a motorway and to make sure that she knew red traffic lights meant stop now, and that speeding up and shooting across a junction on amber shouting "Yippee!" was not a good idea if she wanted to live to be old enough to finish university.

Anyway, we set out. She did all her checks, to impress me I think; mirror, signal, manoeuvre and we pulled out of our avenue, a little too fast for my liking and passed a bit close to some parked cars. We joined the traffic on the main road in a much smaller gap than I would have pulled out in but hey, as she keeps telling me,

"You're getting old, Mum; your nerves have gone." Really? I wonder how that happened.

Lolly wound the window down to wave and shout to some friends who we passed, taking her eyes off the road and veering too much onto the other side in the process. No harm done as there were no cars too close to us now so I checked again to see that the car definitely had air bags as my blood pressure rose a little.

The trouble began when we pulled onto Princess Parkway, a dual carriageway, on the way to the motorway. Lolly stayed in the outside lane. The traffic was busy for the time of day and I noticed a line of vehicles forming behind us. The car behind us flashed his lights. I thought Lolly hadn't noticed. The driver behind us came very close and flashed his lights again and blew his horn. Lolly just ignored this.

"Lolly, pull over into the inside lane, please."

The corners of my daughter's mouth tightened resolutely.

"No, Mum. He can get lost!" she said glaring with narrowed eyes into the rear view mirror. "The sign says 40 miles an hour and that's exactly what I'm doing. I'm not moving over."

One of the cars further back pulled out and overtook us on the inside lane.

"See, just look at that idiot overtaking me on the inside lane. My driving instructor said you're not allowed to do that!"

The driver blew his horn and looked at us crossly as he passed.

"And you can get lost as well, Mate!" my daughter shouted giving the driver a finger gesture. I think she had forgotten I was in the car until I gave her 'the look'.

"Oops... sorry, Mum."

"Lolly," I said patiently, "I know it says 40 miles an hour but very few people stick to the speed limit, especially on here when they are on their way to the motorway. It's lovely that you are keeping the speed limit but just pull over so they can pass."

"I'm not pulling over, Mum. They're breaking the law. That's what's wrong with the world today; nobody obeys the rules that are there to keep us all safe."

I looked at my daughter side-ways, wondering when my grandmother had got into the car and crept into her head.

"What?" she asked.

Another car overtook us on the inside lane and wound down his window to shout abuse at us. The driver behind was now about two inches from our rear bumper, gesturing frantically, red faced with anger and frustration.

"Lolly this is not a very good time to make a point."

"But Mum –"

"Get into the blasted inside lane, now!"

My daughter gave me a hurt side-ways look.

"Alright... no need to shout," she said as she indicated and pulled over. "Mum do you know that you are encouraging these people to break the law."

I looked the other way out of the window, bit my lip and slowly counted to ten.

We duly arrived on the M56 but keeping the speed limit unfortunately was as far as my daughter's good driving went.

"Ooh this is good innit, Mum!" she shouted weaving in and out of traffic and overtaking other cars, far too closely, as if she was on her own personal obstacle course. She had the CD player at full blast and I think the pounding beat of the music was helping to fuel her adrenalin. I was already gripping my seat, gritting my teeth and thinking about making a will.

"Okay, Baby, leave a bit more room between yourself and the car in front and remember how fast you are going... stopping distance. You need a bigger gap when you're overtaking then so many cars wouldn't keep flashing you."

"Oh... is that why they keep flashing me?"

"Er... yes. I think it's the fact that they are having to brake every time you pull out to overtake."

"Oh..." she said.

We took the slip road and came off the motorway to a roundabout, ten miles out of Manchester in order to go back the way we had come. At the roundabout, my daughter, head bobbing up and down to her music put her foot down on the accelerator and kept going without so much as a hesitation.

"Lolly!" I screamed. "That was a roundabout!"

"Was it?" she asked innocently. "There weren't any cars on it, Mum. That's why I didn't realise."

"It's just as well there weren't any cars. You're supposed to stop and give way!"

"I know that, Mum; just chill. I knew it was a roundabout. I was just playing with you. You're sooooo uptight. Chillax parent. I'll stop next time, okay?" I very slowly counted to ten again.

Lolly wanted to go and show her grandmother her new car. We came across my mother and my Cousin Myra a couple of streets away walking back to Mum's house after visiting a friend. Lolly wound the window down excitedly.

"Youooo Grandma! Cousin My!" she shouted as she slammed on the brakes and screeched to a halt, spraying the pavement with water from a puddle. Mum and Cousin My did a spritely jump backwards to prevent being splashed. "I've just been on the motorway. Do you like my new car?"

"Er... yes. It's very nice, Lolly," Mum said, wiping a splash of muddy water from her handbag.

"Dem actually let yu loose on the road now?" Cousin My asked.

"I've passed my driving test now, Cousin My... first time innit Mum? Do you want a lift? Jump in let me take you home."

Mum and Cousin My looked at each other anxiously, then at me.

"Maybe Grandma and Cousin My just want some fresh air, Lolly," I said in an attempt to rescue them. "They've only got to go 'round the corner."

"Er... yes... yes," Mum agreed too quickly. "Don't waste your petrol Lolly.

"Oh it's no problem. Come on both of you, jump in. I'll take you for a drive if you like."

"Er... no... just give us a lift home. That'll be fine," Mum said.

My mother, who is famous for her back seat driving, sat silently on the back seat clutching her handbag tightly on her lap as Lolly shot off like a bullet and screeched around the corner almost on two wheels in Lord only knows what gear. I had to stifle a chuckle as through the vanity mirror, I watched Mum clutching her seat nervously and biting her bottom lip. Cousin My's lips were moving silently as if praying as she looked anxiously out of the window.

"Di house dem pon dis street nice," she remarked to no-one in particular, I think in an attempt to distract herself from Lolly's driving.

"But Lolly, yu caan concentrate on yu driving or hear if anything coming when yu music so loud," Mum said diplomatically.

"Oh it doesn't bother me Grandma but I'll turn it down a little."

By the time we got to my mother's house, Mum and Cousin My both had the same petrified look which I knew was reflected on my face. The tossing about by rapid acceleration and sudden braking had sharply reminded us of our mortality.

"Now I've got my car, Grandma, I can come and take you shopping until I go away to uni," Lolly suggested.

"Er... no, Lolly!" Mum said quickly before I could say anything. "Thank you, Baby, but your mother already knows all the places I like to go for all my little bits and pieces. Don't you, Kelly?"

I nodded with a smile.

I have always thought it really stupid in some films when you see people get off aeroplanes and kiss the ground in gratitude. Believe me, when I got out of Lolly's car with my legs trembling like jelly, I really had to try hard to resist the temptation to drop to my knees and kiss the ground and thank God for my safe deliverance. My daughter, whistling happily, twirled her car key on her finger, brushed a speck of dust from her car and strutted proudly into her grandmother's house.

As I related the speed limit incident on Princess Parkway to my mother and Cousin Myra, as expected, Lolly defended herself strongly.

"Hee hee hee! Lolly keeping the speed limit! That's right; good girl," Mum laughed.

"Well I'm eighteen now, Grandma. Daddy said now I'm old enough to vote I've got to start acting responsibly because if I'm arrested he doesn't have to come and get me out of jail."

"Ha ha ha!" Mum laughed. "Is that right? Get you out of jail for causing an accident or for killing someone?"

"That's not fair, I'm a good driver!" Lolly protested.

"Wasn't it yu mi see nearly kill the puss next door just before yu pass yu test, when yu drive off down the road like rocket under yu tail?"

"I had some new shoes on and my foot slipped on the accelerator, Grandma," Lolly laughed. "I didn't see the cat sitting in the middle of the road. Stupid creature! What a place to sit and clean itself?"

"The poor cat must have seen all its nine lives flash in front of it and I don't think the driving instructor has recovered yet," I laughed. "She had to slam the brakes on and was as white as a sheet. After that, I noticed the neighbours running out when they knew Lolly was having a driving lesson to move their cars out of the way."

"Mum, you're not funny you know. That was only Pete next door and he was just joking. I'm a brilliant driver!"

"Don't take any notice of us Lolly," I said.

"Well you can noh baddah talk," Mum said, "because it's you she get it from."

"Me? What's wrong with my driving?" I asked.

"Is how many times me, Cousin Babsie and everybody else tell you that yu drive like a man."

"Well, I know I'm a good driver and I've never understood exactly what that means," I said feeling a bit offended.

Lolly was cracking up laughing now. I tried 'the look' on her which had always served to get her in order in the past. She just blew me a kiss and laughed even louder. At that moment, my eyes were opened to the fact that my screaming baby had grown up.

"I'm not saying yu not a good driver but I still have to stop you doing anything foolish when I'm in the car wid yu so yu noh kill the two of us. Missus mi noh ready fi goh join John Paul inna Southern Cemetery yet." Mum and Cousin Myra were laughing too now.

"Okay," I said. "So that explains why you are the worse or should I say the best back seat driver on the planet does it?"

"Mi! A must be someone else you talking 'bout. Yu see mi a trouble yu an' yu car except when you nearly launch us through the windscreen on the motorway Lord knows how many times on the way to Dar's funeral." Mum was referring to when I hired an eight-seater people carrier to take us to my Aunt's funeral in London and had a little problem initially with the very sensitive brakes.

"Mi just say enough to stay alive 'til yu bring me back a mi yard inna one piece and mi can thank di Lord, a noh true Myra?"

Mum turned to Cousin Myra and did one of her classic black people 'hee hee hee' laughs.

"Bwoy what is di world coming to eh Mala?" Cousin My answered. "Michael son turn big woman an' a drive car. Hee hee hee!" The rest of the family have always referred to Lolly jokingly as 'Michael's son.'

It has been said by many that we should be aware of what our children are exposed to at an early age, whether bad or good and Lolly is a case in point. Some people who study human behaviour, would go as far as to say be careful what your children are exposed to in the womb because they absorb far more than we think which forms their characters.

My daughter, Lolly has always had a fascination for cars. I wonder if that is due to subconscious memories of being soothed to sleep by her father's midnight car drives in her early months. I also remember when I was pregnant, Laura being very active and kicking strongly while I was driving. She is never more relaxed and comfortable than when she is in a car and often used to go and sit in her father's car when she was upset. She would also sit in the car for hours, studying, saying that was where she could concentrate best.

When my elder daughter, Shari, and I would be in the kitchen or we would go shopping, Lolly could be found with her father, cleaning or tinkering about under the bonnet of his car. From an early age, she had dressed 'like Daddy' in denim jeans, baseball cap and trainers and accompanied Michael to scrap yards and garages and could do a basic service on a car at fourteen with minimum supervision.

It was no surprise to us when Lolly applied for her provisional driving licence as soon as she was seventeen and began lessons. Shari, my eldest daughter, and I to this day can just about put petrol in our cars and air in the tyres. Anything else, and I call Michael or his petite and extremely feminine 'son' Laura to help.

My youngest daughter might drive me mad most of the time but life without her would be too boring to contemplate.

2 Lost

Grandparents in my experience can have more of an influence on their grandchildren than they think even long after they are no longer around. And children in turn can have more of an influence on their parents than they think.

When I was about three years old, my mother got the opportunity to immigrate to England. She was 'sent for' as people were in those days by her older sister, Gwenda, who had previously been sent for by another relative.

After my mother left, I lived happily with my beloved 'Granny' and my cousins in Portland, Jamaica. My grandmother was a no nonsense disciplinarian; a very religious woman with a frighteningly stern outer shell and a soft loving heart which only we, her grandchildren, got an occasional glimpse of. She attended the local Baptist Church every Sunday and never missed Wednesday night prayer meeting. She was always singing softly or humming a hymn... *God will take care of you... Take The Name of Jesus With You...* and my favourite, *The Old Rugged Cross.* I can hear her now... *On a hill far away...hmm... hmm... hmm...*

If any of us misbehaved, she would break off in mid hum and fix us with her steely gaze.

"Pickney, noh mek mi hav fi get a switch to yu backside yu noh?" she would say. The threat was enough.

There is a Jesuit saying which goes – give me a child until he is seven years old and I will show you the man. I am the person I am today not because of my parents but because of my grandmother who influenced my formative years.

When I could barely speak, my grandmother taught me to say grace before eating and to pray before going to bed. Often I would fall fast asleep on my knees, hands still clasped, before Granny finished saying her prayers. One of my older cousins would put her arm around me and hold me up until Granny had finished and they could lift me into bed.

My grandmother taught me responsibility. We all had our jobs around the yard and young as I was, I was expected to do my share, whether it was sweeping up leaves or feeding the chickens, without complaining.

My grandmother always said to me,

"Kelly if yu ever in trouble yu must ask Jesus to help yu, yu hear?"

"Yes mam," I would answer.

My grandmother died and I was sent to England to live with my mother when I was nine years old. While my mother had been in England she had married and had other children. Unfortunately just before I came to England she had separated from her husband so I lived with her and my two little brothers and sister.

After being in England for a while, I noticed that Sundays came and we didn't go to church. We didn't go to prayer meeting. When we ate we didn't say grace or our prayers at bedtime. In fact we didn't have a Bible in our house. In my little nine year old mind that didn't seem right somehow but I didn't like to be disrespectful so I said nothing to my mother who had enough to worry about.

The first time I plucked up the courage to say grace and told my little brother and sister to copy me, they looked at each other and giggled. Mum looked at me in surprise then gave them that same steely eyed 'look' - well known to all West Indian children, which she'd obviously learnt from Granny.

"Shush!" she said to them, "do as your big sister says."

She smiled at me with a strange look on her face.

"Go on, baby," she said. My sister Clara and brother, John Joseph peeped curiously out of one eye at me as they clasped their hands.

"Mum, why yu noh say grace?" I asked. "Granny never used to eat anyt'ing widout saying har grace, yu noh." My mother sighed.

"I haven't said grace for a long time Kelly and it would feel strange to start now," she said. But from then she would sit quietly at the table after serving dinner and nod at me encouragingly as she waited for me to say grace.

"Wha'appen, Mummy, why yu don't say it to, yu farget di words?" I asked one evening.

"No baby," my mother answered. Looking at me she shook her head with a chuckle then closed her eyes and said, "Lord, we thank you for the blessing you send us... great and small."

One night, as I was about to jump into bed as I had done since my arrival in England, an image of my grandmother suddenly flashed into my mind. I knelt down beside the bed and began to say my prayers. My brother and sister who had been jumping on the bed suddenly stopped.

"What are you doing?" my sister, Clara asked.

"Mi saying mi prayers," I answered. They laughed, did somersaults on the bed and threw the pillows at each other until Mum came in to see what the commotion was.

"Kelly's saying her grace," my little sister who was five at the time said. "And we're not even having dinner."

"She's not saying her grace, silly," Mum said. "Come on. Come and kneel down next to your big sister and say your prayers too."

"Mum, why yu noh say yu prayers at night?" I asked as my mother tucked us up in bed. "Granny never used to goh to har bed widout saying har prayers."

"I know, Kelly but I haven't said any prayers for a long time and it would feel strange to start now."

"Mi used to kneel down a night time wid har 'til mi knee dem bun mi yu noh an' mi drop asleep," I continued. My mother looked at me with a strange, sad look on her face as she kissed me goodnight. She sighed heavily.

"I know Kelly, so did I."

But guess what? After a while my mother started kneeling down next to us while we said our prayers.

One day after I had been in England about four months, my mother and my baby brother, Micky, who was about a year old at the time, became ill with flu. My mother lost her appetite after developing a chest infection. She struggled to look after us and a bad cough kept her awake at night. I had to do the shopping and play games with my brother and sister to keep them entertained so mum could rest. Those were the days before computer games and 24 hour television. That was when I started making up stories to entertain my little sister and brother as we couldn't afford many books. I think they found the stories more interesting because of my lilting Jamaican accent which they liked to mimic. I'm still proud of the fact today that I taught them to speak patois.

I wanted to do something to help my mother to get better. When I'd caught a bad cold on my arrival in England, mum had made me chicken soup with little curly dumplings and tucked me up in bed with a hot water bottle. That had made me feel so much better but we had nothing in the cupboard to make soup with because Mum hadn't been well enough to go to the shop in Moss Side where we bought our West Indian food.

"We need chicken, some yam, pumpkin and thyme to make soup, Kelly" mum said. "I can't take the baby out in the cold and the shop is too far away for you to go on your own."

"It noh dat far. Mi catch di bus wid yu before soh mi know where fi get off."

I could tell my mother wasn't sure but after a while she agreed because I think some chicken soup was just what she felt like.

"Don't forget on the way back to get off at Whitworth Park," Mum said, still looking a bit unsure. "Don't take the money out and let anyone see and don't talk to anyone you don't know."

"No mam, mi nah do dat," I answered. "Yu t'ink me stupid like di English pickney dem, Mummy?"

"No Kelly," she said chuckling, as she wrapped my scarf snugly around my neck.

I felt really grown up as I walked to the bus stop clutching my little purse with £5 in it. That was a lot of money in the sixties. I got the bus and bought the things for the soup with no problems.

I skipped happily across the zebra crossing on Alexandra Road and went into Woolworths to buy sweets which mum said I could with the change. That zebra crossing is still there but Woolworths and Miss Fema's shop, which sold West Indian food, are long gone, replaced by houses.

It started to rain as I got on the red double-decker bus to go back home. The conductor squeezed himself past the standing passengers, down the bus collecting fares with his ticket machine swung over his shoulder. The windows of the packed bus steamed up and I realised that I couldn't see where I was going.

After a while, as people got off the bus, I managed to get a window seat but when I wiped a little circle in the condensation on the window and peered out, I didn't recognise anywhere.

"Mi sure seh wi cyaan pass di park already," I thought, *"Mi mus' see it soon."*

The anxious knot in my stomach became tighter and tighter as the bus went along and I wiped a bigger circle on the dirty window but still didn't recognise anywhere. I began to realise with a sinking feeling that I had missed my stop.

The bus went on and on and gradually nearly everyone got off. Then the bus stopped and the few people who were left got up.

"Terminus! Everybody off please!" the conductor shouted. I had to get off the bus because that was as far as it was going. Even though everyone who had got off the bus had quickly disappeared, I wasn't too worried as I stood with my two bags and watched the empty bus drive away.

"No problem! All mi hav fi do is cross di road an' catch di bus going back in di other direction," I thought.

I crossed the deserted street, avoiding puddles and walked along a little way but there were no bus stops on the other side of the road. Then I remembered that where I lived, the buses went one way down Moss Lane East and down Great Western Street coming back. *"A mussi di same up here soh,"* I thought *" Mi wi keep walking down di road til mi see a bus stop."* But there was no bus stop. When I turned to walk back, I couldn't remember which street I had walked down. A few people passed me hunched into their coats with collars turned up and hats pulled down against the cold. I eyed them warily because mum had told me not to talk to strangers. I thought that if I could see a policeman I could ask for directions so I kept walking. I walked and walked until my feet hurt but I saw no policeman and no bus stop.

By this time I was cold, hungry, tired and very frightened as with the sky threatening more rain, I knew it would be dark soon. Then suddenly I remembered that Granny had told me that whenever I was in trouble I should ask Jesus to help me. So I started to pray as I walked along, willing myself not to cry.

"Jesus mi lass yu noh an' mi frighten bad. Please a beg yu help mi!" I looked up and down the street as I finished praying, expecting a policeman to appear. The deserted street of terraced houses stretched out in front of me. Disappointment made the bags feel heavier.

As I turned into the next street, I saw a brightly lit school with children coming out which was strange because my school was off on holiday. There was a *lollipop* lady helping the children to cross the road. Her sign which gave the crossing patrol ladies their name, was held high for oncoming traffic to see. The parents and the children were laughing and chatting to her.

"A wi ask har fi help mi," I thought but having recently come from Jamaica I had a strong Jamaican accent and didn't feel confident talking to anyone white. I stood by the hedge at the side of the road trying to summon the courage to say something and trying hard not to cry. After a while the lollypop lady noticed me and walked over.

"Are you all right love?" she asked. Her kind smile was framed by curly blond hair and a woolly hat.

"Do you want to cross?"

I shook my head.

"Please mam, can you tell me where the 53 bus stop is please? Mi laas!" I blurted out and burst into tears.

"Oh love, you're all right. Don't cry," the lollypop lady said. I'm not sure to this day how she understood what I said to her.

"The 53 bus doesn't run anywhere near here. You're a long way from home," she said when I told her where I lived.

"I'll tell you what. Wait there while I see these children across the road. My sister works in the paper shop over there. She'll soon sort you out."

The lollipop lady took me to the newsagents and explained to the lady in the shop what had happened.

"I'll have to ring the police," the lady said. "They'll take you home, love."

The police! I have never been more terrified in my life. It was all very well asking a policeman for directions but I didn't want them to take me home! I seriously considered running out of the shop but I was so tired and I knew I wouldn't get far with the shopping bags.

"Don't worry luvvy. You don't want to be wondering about out there on an evening like this," the lady who must have been reading my mind said kindly. She gave me some sweets and a drink while we waited for the police. I didn't know what they would say but when the policeman came in his patrol car he was very kind.

"Don't worry sweetheart we'll soon get you home," he said.

Meanwhile at home, I found out later, my mother had been frantic with worry. As the patrol car pulled up she was at the front door wrapping the baby up in his pushchair to go and look for me. I thought my mother would have been angry with me for getting lost but she just hugged and kissed me as if she was going to squeeze all the life out of me.

After the police man had gone, Mum made me a hot drink of Milo and bun and cheese. As she sat watching me eat, she said, "Kelly, for the first time in a long time I got down on my knees today and prayed for Jesus to take care of you and bring you home safely."

"A noh yu one yu know, Mummy," I said taking a big bite of bun and cheese. "Mi pray hard to."

The next Sunday we were up bright and early. Mum had our best clothes ironed and laid out on the bed.

"Is where wi going, Mummy?" I asked.

"To church, baby," Mum said. "I haven't been to church for a long time, Kelly, and it feels strange to be going now, but I think it's time."

It was then I noticed the little parcel next to my clothes and looked at my mother enquiringly.

"Go on, it's yours. Open it," she said. The parcel contained a little white book - *The Bible For Children*, with the inscription:

"To my little Saviour – all my love – Mummy".

It was my most treasured possession for many years.

3 Recycling

My partner, Michael, is an extremely keen recycler although I'm more tolerant of him now after his very philosophical explanation recently. Michael has always been a fairly quiet man who thinks a lot and as a rule doesn't say much, except when he's pursuing his hobby as a disc jockey. When he does say anything, he leaves you with enough food for thought to serve a banquet.

It's all my fault, or so my daughter Laura would have me believe, because I awakened her father's passion, some more unkind souls would say obsession, for recycling. I'd like to think I awakened his passion for a few things but I'm not prepared to take the blame for something as mundane as refuse recycling. Please!

I started recycling and coerced my family into it, when the girls were young and it wasn't a fashionable middle class preoccupation. I thought it was scandalous the amount of recyclable items such as cans and bottles not to mention food that were carelessly discarded by my family when half the world has nothing.

There was just one voluntary group in the area at the time, Emerge, who warned us of the dire consequences for future generations of not preserving vital resources. I thought their thinking sounded noble and a good way of encouraging my family to be more responsible citizens. I ignored the much grumbling in the camp, paid my membership fee to join Emerge and I felt very saintly as I collected my black plastic box and bags. I was younger then and had spare energy to get involved in 'causes'.

You had to actually pay, not much I admit, to recycle before the City Council got in on the act so only true devotees participated with any real enthusiasm. Now some local authorities actually fine you, mightily, for not putting refuse into the appropriately coloured bins. They also fine you for leaving your bins on the pavement too long after they have been emptied. Most people I know, and a know a good few, think it's absolute madness but do politicians ever listen to the masses once they are voted into power? Not in my experience and I've been around a while.

Let me explain how the bin system works so you know I'm not just an old grouch. Where I live each household has a black bin on wheels – a huge monster of a thing known affectionately as 'the wheelie bin'. This is for general rubbish. We have an equally massive green bin on wheels for garden refuse, a slightly smaller blue bin for paper and cardboard and a brown bin for cans and bottles. Hopefully, by now you will have a better understanding of my complaint. On bin days we have a multicoloured forest of bins waiting to be emptied on the pavement of our little avenue; lethal obstacles for anyone who is blind or uses a wheelchair. Every time I look, there seems to be more bins. It's as if the blooming things are reproducing like rabbits, all by themselves.

As if that wasn't bad enough, the City Council delivered yet another bin today - a small grey one for food scraps for composting. I quite like the idea of this actually but still, I think someone in an office somewhere in the Town Hall has too much time on his hands! I am all for saving the environment as I said, but I can't help thinking the officials are missing the point. These bins are made of plastic, a non-biodegradable material, if I'm not mistaken. So, in a million years or so, when we are all dead and gone, all these bins will still be intact! Happily reproducing baby bins, unhindered.

Anyway, back to Michael. He took over from me as the recycling police in our house, since the advent of City Council recycling. I got peed off because I couldn't remember what was supposed to go into which bin and the particular day each coloured bin should be put out for emptying.

The other night I was cuddling up to Michael in bed, as I do, warming my feet on him and just falling asleep when he suddenly turned towards me, jolting me awake.

"Michael! Aww, you made me bite my tongue!"

"Oh sorry… sorry. Hush… hush…Yu wan' mi kiss it better?"

"No!"

"All right... I was only asking. Kelly, I was reading that leaflet the Council dropped through the door when they delivered the new bin today," he said.

"And?" I asked crossly. *You made me nearly bite off my tongue to tell me that*, I thought.

"Well it said that 83km sq of wrapping paper is thrown away at Christmas in Britain every year and 60% of what goes in our bins can be recycled."

"Michael… It's half past eleven."

"Yeah man, I know. Kelly, I was just thinking about the way we recycle memories."

"Uh?" I said. Recycle memories? I thought. Has this man completely lost it?

"What do you mean?" I asked without much interest as I rubbed my injured tongue against my teeth to assess the damage. There was a slight taste of blood but nothing life threatening. I just wanted to sleep.

"Well you can push things to the back of your mind and think you've forgotten them but they always come round and are used again and again to shape us as we mature."

"Really? That's fascinating, babes," I mumbled. *Not*, I thought. *Man, shut up and go to sleep!*

"Well take the black bin."

"Michael!" I said through clenched teeth, "I'd rather not at this time of night, if you don't mind. I want to sleep!"

"Yeah... yeah, I know babes but just listen a minute." What is it about men that when women say 'no', they hear 'yes'.

"The black bin represents hard times," Michael continued undeterred, "experiences that are best left behind but they are still part of us, a by-product of life. Those days when as a student or when you had no job, you had one slice of bread and an egg in the fridge and no money to pay the rent."

I could clearly remember those days so I perked up my ears and started to listen.

"Then there's our green bin. That represents positive memories; the ones that get our adrenalin pumping, maybe scary moments – window pole moments in your case, Kel. You know what I mean?" he added, chuckling. I couldn't resist the urge to pinch him. He was referring to the long wooden pole which we use to open and close the windows. It was my first weapon of choice whenever I thought an intruder might be in the house.

"Aww! Kelly man! You do know what I mean though, don't you?" Michael continued.

"Hmm," I answered, "I suppose so."

" That moment when you got that job, Kel, or when you won that contract when you were up against the big boys, when you first found out you were going to be a parent or you saw your child being born, when... when you realised you were really in love for the first time." He paused. "They... they should really be gold moments; the moments that made us cry or laugh until we cried. Those are positive experiences which raise our self-esteem; memories that we re-create at every opportunity to make us feel good."

"Okay... so... so what about our blue bin moments?" I asked. I was really listening now.

"They are the sad moments Kelly that break our hearts; events that teach us a lesson which we would rather have done without at the time but with hindsight made us stronger, taught us an important lesson about ourselves. The moments we really would like to forget but need to remember."

Michael went quiet again and I could feel his heart beating in the silence as he was clearly reliving one of those blue bin moments. In the dark, I heard him swallow hard. He tightened his arms around me and kissed the top of my head. I felt as if we were having a green bin moment of our own.

"Now let me see," he continued, "brown bin moments are the boring every day things we do but which are important none the less because they give us stability, set boundaries and keep us safe," he said.

"Hmm..." I agreed. I was impressed.

"They reinforce our place in the scheme of things, Kelly. They are the foundation on which all the other memories sit."

It was my turn to swallow the lump in my throat. Michael has always been a pretty smart guy; that's what I like about him but I have no idea when he became such a philosopher.

"Oh Michael... that is such a lovely way to think about it; so where does the new grey bin fit in with the food scraps?"

"Oh that's obvious, Kel; the little scraps of life that don't immediately make sense. You know those moments you mull over, leave to mature, which add richness and spice to life when you realise what they are about. They make you..."

Michael gave a big yawn. With the taste of blood still in my mouth, I ducked instinctively as he lifted his arm.

"Sorry babe... they make you... a more... rounded, interesting person," he said, yawning loudly again.

"I don't think I'll ever look at the bins in the same way again," I said. I lifted my head to kiss him goodnight but his snore made me realise he was already fast asleep. I kissed him anyway.

At the beginning of this year, someone stole our blue bin... don't ask me why but people these days will steal anything that isn't nailed down it seems. Don't even bother nailing anything down, they will just see it as a challenge and cause havoc trying to get the nails out.

One minute the blue bin was there overflowing with assorted papers, the next the bin men emptied it and it was gone. I was secretly glad –

one less bin cluttering up the garden. Outraged, Michael went peeping into all the neighbours' gardens to see if they had more than one but he didn't find it. He asked me to ring the Town Hall for another one but I kept forgetting on purpose. Michael got the message eventually and we started sharing Pete and Jill's bin, next door. They didn't seem to mind because, as I found out recently, Pete and Jill have been taking our old Gleaners and magazines out of the bin to read.

Jill invited me to a coffee morning with her friends from the Mother and Toddler Group she goes to. Not having a toddler or anything even remotely close to one, I was a little surprised to get the invitation. I assumed Jill just needed a hand with making coffee and handing out biscuits so being a good neighbour and a sociable soul, I accepted.

To my amazement I found the women having an animated discussion as they thumbed excitedly through my old copies of Pride magazine which I'd put in the bin the week before. I was mildly amused and puzzled as to what a group of white women could find so interesting in a magazine for black women. I soon found out.

The ladies after welcoming me like an old friend, which immediately made me suspicious, resumed their discussion about black beauty products and their precise use. As the only black person present, I felt out-numbered and didn't really want to be drawn into the conversation. I wasn't given a choice so I held my corner as best as I could and explained that just as they did, we needed specific products to suit our various skin and hair type. I held my corner too well it seemed.

The topic of hair came up next.

"How do bla... er coloured women sit for so long to have those tiny plaits like yours put in their hair?" asked one woman who had been introduced as Sue. She had been sitting at the back of the room rocking her infant in a car seat and hadn't said much so far.

"Oh the time flies by because we usually have some very interesting discussions," I answered. Given my obvious disadvantage, I considered letting the clumsily corrected reference to 'coloured' women pass but unfortunately I've discovered that my tongue appears to work independently from my brain sometimes. "Actually, Sue," I heard myself saying before I could bite the offending organ into submission, "if you don't mind, I prefer to be called black rather than coloured."

"Oh... oh dear... I'm so sorry. I didn't mean to be rude. It's just that I always thought it was more polite to say coloured. I worked with someone once... er when I say worked with... she er... cleaned our office and she called herself coloured. I just thought that was the right word," Sue stammered apologetically. She had gone bright red and I felt a bit sorry that I had said anything especially as all the other women looked a little uncomfortable too.

"There's no need to be embarrassed," I smiled. "I'm not offended and it's not wrong exactly but you know how everyone jumps up and down now about political correctness? I know many of the older generation still do, but it isn't 'PC' to refer to anyone these days as coloured." I had to throw that one in as I knew I was in the company of people who took political correctness very seriously.

"Er... actually," Jill cut in obviously trying to rescue Sue and the situation, "I was watching an American TV programme recently... Opra, I think, and black women were referred to as 'women of colour' which I quite liked. It's a more accurate description don't you think?"

"Why yes, it is," another woman, Amy, said, "because that doesn't specify a colour so it also includes us, doesn't it?" I wasn't too sure about that but hey... I'm all for racial inclusion, so why not?

"Kelly, why do 'women of... er ... colour'," Amy giggled uncertainly at the new expression as she turned the pages of a black hair magazine, "change their hairstyles so often and wear so many wigs and hairpieces and all these... er... unusual colours?"

"Yes, blue and red?" Sue added. The room had suddenly gone quiet again, apart from babbling babies, as the women looked at me expectantly, waiting for an answer.

Now, that question took me by surprise. When I was invited for coffee, this was not the topic of conversation I expected; the weather, weaning babies whatever their colour, nappy rash maybe. I'd often pondered the blue and red hair myself and had debated with my cousin Babsie about her love for gold extensions many times. Babsie's way of ending the debate was, "Chuh, Kelly man! Mi jus' like it, okay, an' mi noh know why dat is a problem to yu."

Had I been in a group of black women... er... sorry, women of colour, I would have immediately replied that it is because most of us are just not comfortable with what God gave us but the reasons behind that is a long story. I couldn't let my sisters down so I used classic stalling tactics so I could think.

"Er... now let me see. That is a very good question, Amy." I took a sip of my Fair Trade coffee and a delicate nibble of my organic chocolate biscuit as I thought about how to phrase my answer without showing my sisters of colour in a bad light.

I keep my hair natural, after years of lost battles with chemical relaxers with my hair being taken as prisoner. It's more convenient to wear it in plaits especially in the winter. The British climate plays havoc with afro-type hair, making it dry and brittle and causing it to break as we move from central heating indoors to the cold and damp outside. Occasionally, I wear a half wig – instant flowing shoulder-length hair. Jill has passed me in the supermarket without recognising me and her dog has barked at me furiously through the hedge until I speak to him and he recognises my voice.

"Do you know, Amy," I said feeling a bit smug as the answer came to me. "We change our hair styles so often simply because we can." The women were clearly taken aback. I don't think they were expecting that. One woman who had been on her way out of the room, with nappy in hand, to change a rather pungent smelling baby, stopped halfway through the door to listen with the wriggling toddler, not caring about his offensive nappy, trying to escape.

"Oh? Because you can?" Amy asked, puzzled.

"Yes. Have you ever noticed the variety of black hair types? African-Caribbean hair is so versatile; we can experiment with different products and styles. It's fun to create new styles. It expresses our individuality and creativity in a way nothing else can."

The women were looking impressed now, nodding and smiling as I got into full swing. The owner of the pungent baby had sat down again with him on her lap. He was protesting loudly but as all mothers learn to do when necessary, we had switched off from his cries and his nappy problem to continue the discussion.

"A lot of what we do with our hair is traditional and cultural. Some of the best social gatherings are in the hairdressers, whether it's an expensive salon or someone's living room."

"That's true," Sue agreed, nodding. "I love going to my hairdressers because I meet people there I don't normally see and I can catch up on the latest gossip."

"I can relax for a while, get away from my husband and the kids and come out feeling like a million dollars," Amy said.

"That's it exactly," I said. "So you see - we 'ladies of colour' do have a lot in common."

"I had my hair plaited with hair extensions in Jamaica though, and I had to take it out as soon as I got back to the hotel because it was so painful," Sue said.

"Personally, Sue, I don't think that kind of plaiting is suitable for European type hair because you would have to plait your hair quite tight for it to stay in," I said.

"You may be right there, Kelly," Sue agreed, "but it looked so nice on the local women. I just wanted to feel part of local culture."

"And I thought hair dressing was just something boring we had to do to look presentable," Jill said. *Hmm...* I thought, feeling pleased with myself. *So did I.*

Jill and her friends had a few other questions, mainly about West Indian food. I found myself explaining the difference between a plantain and a banana, how to cook yam and giving someone a recipe for curried chicken. As the women started to leave, I hoped I had put a few stereotypical ideas about black people firmly to rest for most of them had never spent so long in conversation with a black person.

I couldn't help feeling I'd been set up though and had to ask the question after all the women had gone and I was helping Jill to tidy up. Laughing, Jill blushed and admitted that she had invited me over at the request of the other women who had been fascinated by her tales about me and the fact that, as she put it 'I was not that different from them.'

That evening, Jill knocked on my door with a bunch of flowers in her hand.

"Kelly, I've brought you these as a sort of peace offering to apologise for putting you on the spot like that today. That was just a little bit naughty of me and I really didn't expect it to get so heavy."

"Thank you," I said, "but you shouldn't have bothered, Jill. I really enjoyed meeting your friends."

"Really? Oh great! I've had several phone calls and all of us agree that you were marvellous. It's the most interesting coffee morning we've ever had... er actually no... maybe that was when Jennifer's husband who is now called Jean came... dressed in a mini skirt and high heels. Anyway... they've asked me to say thank you but the flowers are from me. Am I forgiven?"

"Yes, sure Jill. No problem," I said but my mind was running with the image of 'Jean' in high heels.

"Er... we're meeting at Sue's house next week if... okay... perhaps not."

That weekend the men of our family went off to a domino tournament in Sheffield so we girls had a little get together of our own. When I related the coffee morning incident to the female members of my family, my mother, looked at me anxiously.

"A only hope yu not turning into a Uncle Tom yu know," she said. "Yu shouldn't tell dem nut'n. A facey dem damn facey. Wha' dem wan' know 'bout black people fah?"

"But Mum, how do people of one race learn about another if they don't ask questions. We shouldn't get offended."

I had to admit that on one level perhaps Mum was right. Although I had experienced my fair share of racism in England, and had the scars both physical and emotional to prove it, my mother and her generation who came to England in the late forties, fifties and sixties had experienced racism at the sharper end. Those were the days when white people who had rooms to rent, openly had signs in their windows which said, 'No Irish, No Blacks, No Dogs'. There were no laws then to protect us from bigotry.

"I'm not saying yu mustn't be sociable, because Jill is yu neighbour an' that's not how mi raise yu. All I'm saying is, yu have to be careful what yu seh to some people." She stressed the 'some'.

"I know, Mum."

I was still thinking about the subtle dynamics of the relationship between black women and their hair and threw the question out to see what my relatives would make of it.

"Don't you think our hair is almost like a separate entity which we have to coax into good behaviour most days?" I asked.

"Yes," Aunty Bliss said. "Lord knows what mi would do widout my wig because mi cyaan baddah wid hair every day. Talking 'bout recycling, did yu know most a those wigs an' t'ings are made from people hair weh dem cut off?"

"Mi know but Bliss dat noh nut'n new," Cousin Myra chipped in, "black people a recycle hair from Egyptian time. Dem seh the Egyptians weren't black people but mi know seh a lie because is only black people wear wig and have extensions like yu see pon dem drawings don't?" We all had to agree with Cousin My.

"Bwoy di Egyptian dem hair certainly speak loud and clear after all these years an'wi still a plait up and wear wig fi look pretty," my cousin Babsie said.

"Black hairdressing's never been about simple grooming though,

Babs. Never mind the Egyptians, right now our hair makes a bold statement about us to the world," I said.

"Yeah man, yu right there," Cousin Myra said. "Hair can say; in control or on the edge." My made a comical face to illustrate each emotion. "It can say young and frivolous or mature and self confident". Myra's chin rose a little as she patted her hair. "And all the emotional states in between," she added. Mum and Aunty Bliss looked at Cousin My and then at each other with a smile.

"All the emotional states in between," Aunty Bliss whispered to Mum, nodding her head in Cousin Myra's direction. Fortunately Cousin My, who was cutting up a fruit cake she had brought for the occasion, didn't hear.

"Behave yuself and leave My alone," Mum whispered back.

"Some black people hair usually just say, 'should know better' or 'what the hell!'" Cousin Babsie said.

"Seriously though, hairdressing really does play a big part in our culture," I said still laughing. "Look at films likes Barber Shop, where the barber and the hair salon is the heart of the community and families."

"Me and my sisters were very close when we were growing up and we always used to wash and comb each other's hair," Cousin Myra said. "We used to copy all our hairstyles from in the twenties. It brought out my artistic side before I started cake decorating."

"Combing my girls' hair when they were little definitely brought us closer together in a way you can't understand unless you've experienced it," Babsie added. "Yu know a lot of men like doing hair too?"

"Yes, a true. Some a di best hair dressers are men," Mum said. "Well, dem wear trousers anyway," she added.

"Michael has always liked doing our hair," I said. "He says it relaxes him."

Michael had began his exploration into hairdressing when I was heavily pregnant with our daughter, Shari and could barely move.

"Some women married fi years an' dem husband noh know what dem hair look like. Is a good t'ing too because dem husband would run if dem see dem without di wig," Aunty Bliss laughed.

"I used to work with a woman," Mum said, "an' she posh, she posh so til. She always dress up like dress puss wid long hair down har back. One day I had to goh to har house for somet'ing an' a tell yu, Missis, if mi heart noh did strong when mi see har widout di make-up and hair mi would an' put mi foot ina mi hand and run. Mi seh di woman noh even have har own teet dem!"

Of course by now we were all cracking up with laughter while Mum just stood with a little mischievous smirk on her face.

"But we recycle everything already yu know," Cousin Myra said. "Yu just have to wait long enough for t'ings to turn fashion again. We recycle music an' even di dance dem wi di bwoy dem a do pon TV. Yu look good when dem a dance if yu noh see di same moves from dem old film weh show African people a dance. A tribal dance di bwoy dem a do like it ina dem blood."

"Well, look 'ere noh," Aunty Bliss said. "Talking about hair, yu noh know di difference between a black woman an' white women when dem making love?"

"Ah right Bliss, let's keep t'ings decent now," Mum said. "Yu figet Kelly and Babsie is here?"

"Is all right man, mi not telling dem nut'n dem noh know already. Listen noh," Aunty Bliss replied. Cousin Babsie and I looked at each other with raised eyebrows but said nothing.

"Di white woman seh to har husband, 'Darling you can play with my hair if you like'," Aunty Bliss continued. "Soh har husband mess up har hair. Him push it left and right an' north and south 'til him please an' di two of dem happy -" Babsie's loud snort of laughter cut Aunty Bliss off in mid tale. Aunty Bliss turned and slapped her playfully. "Yu noh hear yu Aunt Mala seh fi keep it clean," she said. That just got the rest of us who had been trying to keep a straight face, laughing and a louder snort of laughter from Babsie. Aunty Bliss who could hardly keep a straight face herself continued her story.

"Listen... listen noh man. Unnuh stop laugh an' listen. Di black woman now, she seh, 'Baby yu can play wid anyt'ing yu like but if yu touch me blouse n skirt hair weh mi jus' pay £100 fi do, mi a goh kill yu." This time no-one could hold back the laughter. We laughed until tears ran down our faces.

"Anyway, joke aside, Kelly," Mum said, wiping her eyes. "Mi know yu noh fool fool an' yu understand exactly what mi mean 'bout yu neighbour Jill an' har fren dem. Mi in dis country a long time an' mi on dis earth longer than yu. When yu t'ink seh yu an' some people a fren dem tek every word an' use it against yu. Before yu know it – bam! Dem turn us ina slave again."

"Okay, Mum. I'll be careful," I said. There was no point arguing. I have never won an argument with my mother and today wasn't looking good.

"Women of colour?" Mum laughed. "Whatever next Lord? Soh wi noh black noh more? One minute wi mulatto then wi coloured, wi half caste then wi mixed race and duel heritage. Backside, wi turn rainbow now!"

"Well you can blame Michael," I said. "Since Shari had Issy he's been on a one man crusade to preserve the planet for future generations. I wanted just to throw all those magazines in the black bin but he insisted I had to put them in Jill's blue recycle bin."

"I think Michael's right. We all have to do our bit to save the planet and to get on with each other, Kelly, no matter what our colour," Cousin Myra said."

"Well, we might as well," Mum said. "All the world leaders dem doing is having meeting to decide if dem fi have meeting fi talk 'bout global warming while dem caan see seh di North an' South Pole a melt an' wash wi weh."

I had to smile. My family had come up trumps once again, adding their unique personalities and perspectives in my continuing education on life and its peculiarities. Who would have thought recycling some old magazines could result in such an interesting race relations summit with the women from my neighbour's Mother and Toddler Group. Not to mention my family's quirky opinion on the subject.

What I've discovered each time I've raised the issue is that recycling inadvertently plays a much bigger part in our lives than we think with there being many different, often hidden aspects to it. Everything has its time; the earth continually regenerates whether it's on a small or large scale, death and rebirth is something we can't get away from. So like Cousin Myra said recently, maybe everything is unfolding just as it should and global warming is nothing unnatural to be afraid of, rather something to be accepted as inevitable as the earth recycles itself.

4 In The Mix

"Who left the front door open?" my mother asked, coming in.

"Michael is out there. Didn't you see him sorting out the rubbish for recycling?" I asked.

"Hmm... recycling is all right but yu better mind one a these days Michael don't recycle you," Mum said, kissing her teeth. "Him run goh put ring pon Leslie finger but a notice him still noh put noh ring pon your finger." Unfortunately, Michael came through the door at that moment. He looked at us both. If I had the power to turn back time, that is a moment I would have turned back and erased not to see the pain on Michael's face. Without a word he opened the door to the basement and disappeared down the stairs. I turned away from my mother and walked across the room in exasperation, leaning against the kitchen sink.

"Mum, how many times have I told you" I began. I stopped in mid sentence. Mum and I looked at each other as the piercing strains of a saxophone drifted upwards through the floor. All the energy seemed to go out of me at once.

"Told me what!" Mum shouted.

"Nothing," I said, shaking my head.

"So yu shouting at me now fi nothing. A wha' wrong wid Michael anyway? All I said was – "

"Yes, okay, Mum. We heard what you said. Just leave it now, please," I said fighting back the tears.

"Yu faadah would turn –"

"Yes! Daddy would turn in his grave if he could see me now. By your account, he's been spinning none stop since we buried him because of all the things I've done!" To my surprise my mother started to laugh.

"What?" I asked, puzzled.

"Well yu faadah did always like dancing yu know," Mum said. I shook my head in disbelief but couldn't help smiling.

"I'm sorry," Mum said, patting my hand. "Don't get upset. I didn't mean what I said."

"I know."

"Do you think I should apologise to Michael? I don't understand what's going on between the two of you but I know he's not a bad man."

"Yes, I do think you should say sorry but not right now, okay. Put the kettle on and let's have some tea."

Michael has what he calls his 'den' in the basement of our house. Our two daughters, Shari and Lolly, and I learnt a long time ago not to go down there without his express permission unless we're looking for trouble.

"If you disturb the air down there Daddy knows," Lolly says.

The den, which is behind Michael's office, has his reclining easy chair with footrest, a mini refrigerator stocked with his favourite lager and in a corner, his exercise equipment. Occupying one half of the den is Michael's custom built music system. Next to this are thousands of vinyl records, tapes and CDs, along with his other memorabilia from his days as the radio presenter, Deejay Mixer, in London. If it's anything to do with music from reggae to hip hop, Michael has it – carefully labelled and in its place.

Occupying pride of place in the den is Michael's saxophone. Every now and then, when he is particularly moved by something, he retreats to his den and we are treated to an impromptu soul stirring performance. Michael expresses his emotions with his saxophone in a way that pierces the heart, melting you from the inside out. He also plays his saxophone if he thinks I'm angry with him because he knows I can't stay angry after listening to those pleading notes coming up through the floor. I guess it must be his idea of music soothing the savage beast. It works for anger but not sorrow.

It was the early hours before I felt Michael climb into bed next to me. He slipped his arms around me and I snuggled close to him without a word being said.

Michael and Mum didn't speak for about a month although to give her credit, she made several attempts to apologise. Michael was having none of it. Complex emotions which had lay dormant, now having been given a voice by my mother, rose to the surface and demanded attention. The atmosphere in our house was tense.

Since my mother has raised the subject in her own inimitable style, I think it's time for me to explain my relationship with Michael. To tell the truth, Michael and I had sort of 'recycled' each other. We met at school and his passion since I've known him has been music. He played the saxophone in the school jazz band but we never spoke until Mr Mallow, the music teacher, heard me audition for the school Christmas play. I didn't get the part but the jazz band was looking for a singer and I couldn't believe it when Mr Mallow asked me afterwards if I was interested in singing with them. I love singing and can hold a tune but I'm not what you'd call a great singer. I felt honoured because the jazz band was Mr Mallow's pet project. He had taught its members to play their instruments from Year 7 when they entered the school.

Michael was one of the popular boys who had his fair share of female admirers. He had a string of girlfriends whom he frequently traded in or they traded him in. I think I was the envy of a lot of girls in our school but personally I didn't fancy him. At least that was what I told myself at the time. Although we became friends through the jazz band, he was two years older and I never thought in a million years we would end up together. Michael was my first real boyfriend and we never felt the need to 'trade each other in'.

One day in between girl friends he asked me if I fancied going to a concert he had tickets for. I had never heard of Bob Marley and the Wailers in those days – not many people outside of Jamaica had. The concert was great and the rest is history as they say. I remember being very impressed by the backing singers, 'The I Threes' and spent days perfecting Rita Marley, Judy Mowatt and Marcia Griffiths' dance then teaching it to my friends.

It was after this that Michael became friends with the guys who played the music at the local youth club and started playing out at gigs with them. He was a natural deejay who had the hall jumping every time he took charge of the turn tables. He was part of Empress Sounds back in the days of the big sound systems like Killer Man Taurus and Baron Hi Fi who played at the old West Indian Centre at Carmoor Road. That was before the new centre at Westwood Street was built. Those were the days when each area, like Moss Side, Old Trafford and Longsight had its sound system and its followers, instead of gangs and the systems competed against each other. Michael became known as DJ Mixer and the name stuck. He's still better known today by his nick name, Mixer.

The reason Michael and I aren't married is... complicated, as they say. Michael at seventeen had been in the last year of his 'A' levels when we got together. I later went on to do my 'A' levels too but like the children of most other black families at the time, I couldn't afford to go to university. Unable to go to university either, Michael had taken the long drawn out route of working where he could and studying part-time to become a building surveyor.

When I was twenty, I got pregnant. I had been on the City Council waiting list for a flat for a couple of years and was offered a one bedroom flat on the twelfth floor of a multi storey block the same week I found out I was pregnant. Not wanting to go back on the waiting list for family accommodation I signed up for it.

I wasn't forced to leave home but I felt it was for the best. Michael and I decorate the flat. With some financial help from my mother and the little I had managed to save, we bought basic furniture and bubbling with excitement, I moved into my first home. Michael spent most of his time with me when he wasn't working or at college. He helped me out financially as much as he could but I refused to let him move in because I felt he had enough to cope with and I was frightened that our relationship wouldn't stand the strain.

"Yu faadah would an' turn in him grave if him could see yu wid dat big belly and no ring on yu finger," my mother said. "Mi noh know wha' yu an' Michael a gwaan wid. Him faadah need fi talk to him. If yu faadah was alive this could never happen."

"Mum, I'm fine," I said. "Michael and I are happy just as we are."

My hair, as afro-Caribbean hair has the ability to do, took on a life of its own during pregnancy – the life of a spoilt, temperamental child that I could not control. My mother wasted no opportunity in telling me –

"A good! Yu a woman now; a who tell yu fi goh trouble big people somet'ing if yu can't manage it?

I had been struggling with shampoo and conditioner in the bathroom for over half an hour and getting more frustrated by the minute. As I tried to comb out my hair, the comb stuck fast. It snapped as I pulled at it angrily and one half flew across the bathroom. That was the straw that broke the camel's back. My back ached, my feet were swollen, places I don't want to mention ached. I slid to the floor and burst into tears. Not the dainty sniffs as seen on TV but loud child-like sobs. I wanted my mum. Miserable as she could be, she would have hugged me and made me feel better.

I was so deep in misery that I didn't hear Michael come into the bathroom. I just felt his arms around me helping me up which believe me was not an easy task with gravity and a huge belly working against us.

"Come on Kel don't cry. It's not that bad."

"How do you know; you're a man! You just get the fun part!" I shouted. I think he was referring to my hair but I was referring to pregnancy.

"I'll do it for you," he said, ignoring my outburst. Michael was used to my raging hormones by now which had sharpened my tongue to a precision edge. Now if men could have babies for us wouldn't that be wonderful! I'd make sure they have a baby three times a year. That would fix them.

It was a measure of my emotional state that I actually let Michael loose anywhere near my hair. I was past caring. To my surprise he dried, combed, greased and plaited, humming away to himself while I sniffed, blew my nose and complained loudly that he was pulling my hair out at the roots.

Michael would have dropped the comb and ran out of the house if he could have read my mind and see all the evil plans I was hatching for him, including a do-it-yourself vasectomy, if he ever came near me again. By the time he had done half my hair, I had decided on separate beds, then separate houses. Separate planets started to look good until I decided I needed to get a grip on reality. It's a good thing memory is selective and once women give birth, in most cases, the pain is veiled behind the haze of pleasure the new born baby brings, or the human race would be extinct. I wonder if any woman has ever been acquitted of murdering her child's father on a plea of child birth? You know how the French have 'crimes of passion'. Would this be a 'crime of pain' I wonder or just plain old insanity.

"And what made you murder your husband so brutally, Mrs Smith?"

"Your Honour, I battered him to death because he wanted sex and I suddenly remembered giving birth to our 9lb son."

"Very well Mrs Smith. Case dismissed on grounds of child birth."

By the time Michael finished my hair, I had a splitting headache to go with my other aches and my head was so sore I could barely touch it. With a big grin on his face, he held the mirror up proudly for me to have a look. I hadn't expected perfection but what I saw was a shock believe me and was probably the reason Shari was born two weeks early. Sorry Michael... only joking! A mixture of half plaits and twists stuck up from my head from every possible angle. He had put almost the entire jar of hair grease in my hair and I looked as if someone had dragged me through a thorny hedge, twice.

"Er... it's not the way you would have done it but it's alright for a first try isn't it?" he asked. Mouth wide open, I looked up into his anxious face and fell in love with him all over again.

"Thank you, baby," I said, reaching up to give him a hug. "It's fine," I lied.

"If I just put a bit more hair grease on this bit –" Michael began.

"No!" I shouted. "It's fine!"

With a little practice, Michael became an expert hairdresser, under my tutelage. He even got adventurous and started straightening and styling my hair after swearing me to secrecy. He didn't want any of his friends to know but I didn't see a problem with that, after all I'd been plaiting his hair in cane row since the days of the jazz band at school.

Our daughter Charlotte was born in 1979. She wasn't planned but she wasn't a mistake either. She was a blessing straight from God's hand.

I've never been married but Michael was for a number of years, hence the ten years difference between our daughters' ages. He calls those his dark years when he was trying to be, and nearly made it as one of the first black disc jockeys on British National Radio.

Michael was in the final year of studying to become a building surveyor when he was offered a job as a presenter with one of the big radio stations in London. He was well known locally from his days with Empress Sound System, on the night club circuit and as a local radio presenter. This was the big break he had been waiting for.

Of course, he wanted Shari and I to go with him but I had just got a good job with the local authority and settled Shari into a nursery. I couldn't easily leave that and my family behind for the unknown in London. I had never liked London having spent long periods of my summer holidays there with my Aunty Dar and her daughter, Petal. London was okay in short spells but I didn't want to live there. The pace of life is too fast and the southerners are not as friendly as northerners. Give me Manchester any day.

Michael decided it was an opportunity he couldn't miss. His parents weren't happy about him walking away from his studies or leaving Shari and I behind. I wasn't thrilled either, but I knew how much this opportunity meant to him and felt I should support him in following his dream. We agreed that he would go alone and come home at weekends. Of course, that didn't work because weekends when he was suppose to come home were his busiest times for networking and getting himself known in the right circles. When he wasn't working he quickly got caught up in a world of parties and all that went with the entertainment lifestyle.

Hindsight is a wonderful thing my mother always says. I now know that I should have gone with him to London. The inevitable happened. When he found the time to come home he was so exhausted that he slept most of the time, then he talked excitedly about a world that was completely alien to me. After a while we had little to talk about and Michael became someone I hardly recognised. When he came home he played with Shari. I played with Shari. We played with Shari together but the chasm between us grew. It wasn't easy to watch the love of my life, my childhood sweetheart near enough, slip away without being able to do a thing about it. It felt as if my heart was slowly freezing up inside me.

I knew before he told me when he met someone else. She was white, moved in the right circles and was good for his career in a way I could never be. He was worried that I would stop him from seeing Shari but even if that had entered my head, I couldn't do it to my little daughter.

A year after he left Manchester, a Michael with a pierced ear and bleached blond hair who had lost so much weight that I hardly recognised him, came to tell me that he was getting married to Leslie, his new girlfriend. He said he wanted to tell me himself before I heard it from anyone else. The slow freezing process which had began inside me months before was completed that day.

I expected a reproachful 'I told you so' from my mother but all she said was,

"You know your room is still here if you want to give up the flat and come home, Kelly. We can easily rearrange the furniture to fit a little bed in for Shari and we'll be able to help you with her." I was touched but I loved my little flat and it had too many happy memories to walk away.

If those were Michael's dark days, for me they were a black hole. My wonderful wacky family took it in turn to keep me distracted in the first weeks when meaningless hours permeated with pain rolled into days and Shari was the only reason I got out of bed. Gradually a demanding job and caring for my daughter dulled the edge off the pain enough for me to get through the day without dissolving into tears.

Shari was a flower girl. She talked constantly about the wedding and couldn't understand why I wasn't marrying her Daddy. I fixed a smile on my face and tried to explain to her as best as I could even though I couldn't understand it either. I focussed on work and looking after Shari who kept me sane until after a long time I found myself laughing and finding joy in life again but inside my heart stayed frozen.

After Michael got married he asked for Shari to come and spend weekends with them. My first reaction was, *"Like hell I will!"* Then I thought about it and realised I would just be hurting Shari so I agreed on condition that I met 'the wife' and saw where my child would be staying.

Leslie wasn't at all the way I imagined. I expected her to be middle class, classy, confident and patronising. She was middle class and classy but she seemed really nervous and went out of her way to be nice, assuring me that she would take good care of Shari and I could phone her and Shari could phone me anytime. Shari seemed to like her so I was satisfied if not happy. She had a beautiful bedroom at Michael's house with everything a little girl could want and I swallowed my feelings of irritation reminding myself that Shari had a nice bedroom at home with more toys than she knew what to do with.

To give Michael his due even though I had a well-paid job and wasn't short of money now, he made sure we wanted for nothing. My mum said it was guilt and it was the least he could do but by now counselling had helped me to move beyond bitter so I could smile at that. It was because the counselling sessions helped me so much to come to terms with the unforeseen turn my life had taken, that I decided to train to become a counsellor myself. After Shari was born Michael and I had been so happy 'playing dolly house' as Mum called it. I had thought that we would be together forever. I had just taken it for granted that we would get married one day but we weren't in any hurry.

Michael lived in London for six years, working at the radio station and as a deejay in various night clubs before the cracks in his glamorous lifestyle began to show. I suspected something was seriously wrong when he started making excuses about Shari coming to stay with him and Leslie. The excuses he gave Shari was that Leslie was either tired or ill but he never discussed his relationship with me. Instead he began to visit Manchester more often to see Shari, staying with his parents but when he picked Shari up, he looked even thinner and stressed. He had also started smoking heavily and I suspected drinking more alcohol than he should.

On occasions I had to ring Michael so that Shari could speak to him. It was the days before mobile phones. Whenever Leslie answered the phone she was pleasant and polite but the strain in her voice was obvious and a couple of times her speech sounded slurred as if she had been drinking.

We didn't see Michael for a couple of months which was very unusual but he rang Shari every couple of days. Then, Michael's younger sister, Joan, popped in to see us one evening and out of the blue, she told me that Michael had left his job at the radio station and was back in Manchester. He and Leslie weren't together anymore. I should have been happy but I wasn't. I'd got to know Leslie and I knew what she must be going through after all it wasn't her fault Michael and I had split. If it hadn't been her it would have been someone else. I can say that about her now but believe me that wasn't how I felt at the time.

Once people found out he was back, Michael was in demand to play at functions and took up his old slots again on the local radio station, Real Reggae FM. He also started helping out at the West Indian Community Centre. In no time at all it was as if Michael had never left Manchester.

Having lost interest in becoming a surveyor, Michael threw himself into establishing a building business with his brothers, Matthew and Mark, AKA Skin and Bones. His mum, Portia, kept me updated every time I took Shari round to see her.

It was two years before we got back together with a little help from Shari our matchmaker. I had saved enough for a deposit and had bought a little two bed room house by then. Michael began to visit more and more often to see Shari until he was coming almost every evening. As it was usually about dinner time, I offered him dinner occasionally. Then he was eating with us every time he came because Shari would invite him to.

"You have to ask Mummy if that's ok," he would whisper. Of course I had to give in to Shari's pleading eyes. She asked him one evening to stay and read her a bedtime story.

"Please Daddy. I have to read my own now because Mum said I'm too old for bedtime stories." Again, the answer was,

"Only if it's okay with Mummy." The pleading eyes got me again. I couldn't help smiling as they raced each other up the stairs with Michael picking Shari up half way up the stairs and running the rest of the way with her under his arm.

They spent about half an hour reading and laughing. After a while, not hearing a sound from upstairs, I peeped into Shari's room to see Michael lying across her bed… fast asleep.

"Ssshhh… Mum. I read Daddy a story and he fell asleep. Can he stay until morning… please?" She had removed her father's shoes, tucked her quilt and soft toys all around him and was lying with her head resting on his chest exactly the way I used to. It brought a lump to my throat.

"No, baby; he can stay for a little while, until you're asleep. Then he has to go home to Nanna's house."

About an hour later Michael came downstairs carrying his shoes.

"Sorry, Kel, I fell asleep," he said sheepishly.

"I know," I said.

Eventually I did allow him to stay until morning. Almost immediately I became pregnant with Lolly. Well meaning 'friends' told me I was mad to take Michael back; the same friends whose husbands had 'secret' women and children who they pretended not to know about. When I asked Mum's opinion, she began to hum softly the way she usually did when she was thinking and didn't say anything for a while.

"Yu know you've never stopped loving Michael, Kelly. That's why between yu and Shari, yu run every man who come anywhere near yu. Real love is hard to find nowadays. Stop punishing yourself and Shari. She need har father. A yu have to live wid Michael, not yu fren dem."

…   …   …   …

"Michael *has* asked me to marry him. Why won't anyone believe me, Babsie?" I asked. I was at my cousin's house teaching her to make sweet potato pudding and getting annoyed because she wasn't doing anything I was telling her to do.

"I believe yu because mi already know seh yu fool fool but why would Aunty Mala? Would anyone in their right mind in your position say 'no'?

"Well, I have never actually said no, you know. I've just never … er… said yes either."

"Well that noh mek noh sense to me. If yu ask me I t'ink yu need that head of yours seeing to."

"It's funny you should say that because I've decided to see a counsellor again. I had my first session yesterday." Babsie stood looking at me with a puzzled expression.

"But you are a counsellor soh how come yu a pay fi see counsellor. All yu have to do is stand up and look at yourself in a mirror and talk to yourself don't? That would work because then yu noh even have to wonder what yu mean or what yu thinking because yu would know already. Yu noh see it?"

"You're not serious?"

"Of course mi serious! Yu noh need fi pay someone to talk to, Kelly. When yu done talk to yuself you just write yuself a cheque and yu don't even have to cash it... perfect! Job done!"

"Babsie..." I laughed incredulously. "It doesn't work that way."

"Ahright then. Look 'ere. Just sit down here. Mi wi talk to you for free an' tell you what to do. Yu can tell mi if mi doing anyt'ing wrong. Yu can all pay mi if it wi mek you feel better an' all include tip to if yu t'ink seh mi give yu good advice. Anyway, what did the counsellor say?"

"Nothing... she's just talking a load of rubbish if you ask me. She said that subconsciously, I have never really forgiven Michael for leaving me and marrying someone else and I will never be able to move on until I do if I can't even bring myself to talk to him about how I feel."

"Well she got that right! Lawd she good een? But yu pay har fi tell yu dat? Mi could an' tell yu dat free."

"Well you'd be talking rubbish too!" I answered.

"Kelly mi know yu better than yu know yuself an' mi know from Michael come back from London, yu an' him noh talk 'bout why yu split up. Kelly, all these years you t'ink seh him only come back because of Shari and stayed because you got pregnant with Lolly." I opened my mouth to protest but Babsie held up her hand to stop me.

"First Shari got married and left home and now Lolly leave and gone to university you think it's only a matter of time before Michael leave too, right?" Babsie said, emptying half a package of flour into the pudding mixture while I was getting nutmeg out of the cupboard.

"I've never heard such rubbish in my life! Babsie I said 8 ounces not the whole bag of flour! What is wrong with you?" I shouted as I noticed what she had done.

"Why yu soh miserable man? Mi caan remember how much flour yu say to measure! Yes, the counsellor is spot on!" Just then Babsie's husband Ferdie came into the kitchen to see what all the shouting was about.

"What's wrong wid di two a yu why unnuh a mek up soh much noise in here?"

"Ferdie yu ever si such a miserable, hard ears woman?" Babsie complained.

"But Babsie, you're not listening to a word I'm saying. You can't follow the simplest instructions!" I shouted.

"Kelly wha' yu bothering mi head fah man? I'm listening to every word you're saying but if mi could follow simple instruction mi would an' learn fi cook long time don't?"

"Hmm... look like Mixer mustn't be playing him saxophone to Kelly's satisfaction lately," Ferdie said.

"Yu know!" Babsie said, kissing her teeth.

"What's that suppose to mean?" I demanded but they ignored me.

"A Kelly a baddah Michael head," Babsie said laughing. "Poor t'ing getting old. Yu notice all di grey hair dem ina him head lately? But yu know wha dem seh, Ferdie?"

"No. Wha' dem seh, baby?"

"There's many a good tune played on an old fiddle hee hee hee!"

"Old saxophone yu mean ha ha ha! Babsie, noh do Mixer soh man. Maybe him just need fi change di tune or him need a little oil fi loosen up any rusty parts on him instrument."

"Ha ha ha! Mek Kelly sing a new song wid some high notes yu mean! Den she might say 'yes' next time him ask har fi marry him."

"Ahhh! See it deh! Well Babs dem seh a change is as good as a rest."

"Excuse me, I'm still here! And yu not funny!" I shouted but they just continued to ignore me.

"Yu hear somebody say somet'ing Babs?"

"No sah. Mi noh hear nut'n. Maybe Kelly need a change if she and Michael nah mek sweet music together no more. Mi t'ink a nice gold ring pon har finger is just what she need."

"Maybe she need di ring but she noh need noh change, man. She have exactly wha' she want."

"Yu t'ink Michael need some help den?"

"No man. Mixer can handle him business."

They went on like this for a good ten minutes laughing at each other's jokes at my expense while I tried to rescue the pudding, until I was forced to physically push them both out of the kitchen. As I closed the kitchen door, I couldn't help laughing too.

"You got that right Ferdie," I said quietly. "I do have exactly what I want and he's not slipping away this time."

"No baddah gwaan stush in there!" Babsie shouted on the other side of the door. "Wi can hear yu a laugh. Yu better run gwaan home goh mek puddin' wid Michael an' shout, 'yes!' as loud as yu can, before him run way lef yu again."

It took a few minutes of searching among the contents of my handbag before I located my mobile phone at the bottom. I was smiling but I had a strange nervous flutter in my stomach as Michael's number started to ring.

There had been a tense atmosphere in our house long before Michael overheard my mother talking about his ex-wife. That incident had been the badly needed catalyst which had spurred our relationship into the next phase. Michael and I had been politely tip-toeing around each other as we carried our pain and pretended all was well. The children which had cemented us together had now flown the nest. Babsie was right, now Lolly had gone away, we no longer had a buffer between us. It was make or break.

When Michael answered the phone I could hear the apprehension in his voice due to the argument we had had that morning.

"Er... I was just wondering what time you're finishing today," I said.

"I've got a few things to finish off but nothing that can't wait until tomorrow. Why?"

"Michael, can I take you out to dinner?" I asked. There was silence on the other end of the phone. He definitely had not been expecting that.

"Kelly, are you asking me out on a date?"

"Er... yes... I suppose I am," I laughed.

"Well how can I refuse an offer like that? It's a long time since I heard you laughing."

"We need to talk and resolve some issues that have been hanging over us for a long time, Michael."

"Yes, I know," he said.

Michael and I talked for a long time and the wound that had been politely festering for years was finally cleaned, cauterised and set on its way to healing. As we sat over our umpteenth cup of coffee, he took a small black velvet box from his pocket. I had anticipated this because he had been shuffling about on his chair, looking uncomfortable and putting his hand in his pocket and taking it out again empty for about half an hour. Inside the box was a diamond ring. To my embarrassment he slid onto one knee on the floor.

"Kelly, I bought this for you over fifteen years ago. You know how much I love you. Will you marry me?" Michael looked around at the other people in the restaurant who were politely pretending not to look and added, "Yu cyaan shame mi in 'ere by saying no, man."

This time I took my cousin Babsie's advice and did a slightly tamer re-enactment of that famous scene from the film 'When Harry Met Sally'.

"Yes! Yes!" I shouted. The other people in the restaurant burst into spontaneous applause as I threw my arms around Michael.

"Now we've embarrassed ourselves, get up and let's get out of here," I whispered.

5 The Flood

"Water, water, everywhere and not a drop to drink."
The day my youngest daughter Laura (Lolly) quoted her version of the verse taken from Samuel Taylor Coleridge's story of *The Rime of the Ancient Mariner*, as we watched rain pouring down, little did we realise just how apt it would prove to be before the end of the day.

Why is it as human beings we find water either fascinating or terrifying? Is the fear and fascination of water born of subconscious memories of the flood as related in the Christian Bible, the cleansing of the earth and destruction of the antediluvians? Or is it plain and simply that we know too well the two very different sides of the awesome substance which covers approximately seventy per cent of our planet's surface? Water can be a calming, healing friend one minute and an angry mighty enemy the next, snatching lives, causing devastation as it wipes out huge swathes of civilisation.

God apparently anticipated this fear and according to the *Bible*, to reassure Noah, his family and their descendants, He made them a promise that He wouldn't cleanse the earth again using water. He gave them a sign of this promise - a rainbow, to dispel our anxieties.

"Bwoy, Lolly, even duck would an' get depress an'kiss dem teet' today," my mother remarked, as my extended family sat despondently in my living room, wherever they could find space, watching the monsoon-like rain beat noisily against the window.

"Typical British weather," my Uncle Al remarked, kissing his teeth. "Waste a time planning anyt'ing; rain stop play every time."

We were surrounded by bags and baskets from which exuded mouth watering aromas of fried chicken, fish and all things Jamaican and spicy. Today was supposed to be our family picnic at Lyme Park to celebrate my mother's 70th birthday. A lot of planning had gone into it for months to ensure everyone could be present. I usually like rain, although obviously not today.

"Oh what a shame eh Mum?" my brother John Joseph (JJ to us) said. "It's spoilt your birthday."

"No, man, it noh spoil nut'n. It's nice that you all made the effort to be here fi mi birthday rain or shine. I have to thank the Lord because I never thought I'd live to see seventy. Life don't come wid noh guarantee yu know, John Joseph."

My three year old grandson, Issy, wondered around all the bags with a thoughtful expression on his face.

"Grandma can't go outside in the rain without her wellie boots because she'll get her feet wet and catch a cold," he remarked.

"That's right, baby," I said.

"Are we having a picnic at home then, Nanny?" he asked.

"No, Issy," I answered. "We're just waiting for the rain to stop."

"Mum, that's a really good idea!" Lolly cried."Why don't we have a picnic here? Even if the rain stops now it'll be too wet in the park for a picnic."

"Hmm... why not?" my partner Michael said. "We can just move all the furniture into the dining room, spread the oilskin sheet on the carpet and put the table cloth on top like we would have done at the park."

"We can put all the children's bean bags and cushions on the floor to lounge on," my cousin Barbara (aka Babsie) added. I must admit, what at first seemed like a silly idea was beginning to sound appealing.

"No man mi cyaan baddah wid that," my aunt Beverley (Bliss) said. "From Al mek mi fall down last Christmas an' mash up mi knee, mi noh t'ink mi can sit down pon floor. Let's just put everything on the dining room table and eat."

"Oh come on Aunty Bliss. Where's the fun in that?" JJ asked.

"Don't be such a spoil sport Aunty Bliss. Where's your spirit of adventure?" Lolly added.

"Ah right! Unnuh noh baddah gang up pon mi. Is up to Mala; a fi har birthday."

"A t'ink it's a nice idea," Mum said, to my surprise. "We eat round di table all di time. Di pickney dem wi like it."

So that was settled. The men moved the furniture into the dining room and we covered the carpet in a corner of the room and laid the food out. Lolly and my eldest daughter, Shari brought all the bean bags and a couple of folding chairs from the basement for Mum and Aunty Bliss.

Michael seized his opportunity and went into DJ mode, putting on the CD for Mum which we usually pulled out for such occasions.

"Happy birt'day to yu!" Uncle Al sang along at the top of his voice with Stevie Wonder. Before we knew it Mum's birthday picnic was in full swing while the rain continued to beat down outside.

"I have just the thing for you, Mum," Michael said. "Soon come." He disappeared and returned a few minutes later with his pride and joy from his den in the basement – his old turn tables. With Uncle Al and Ferdie helping, Michael brought up boxes of old vinyl records and set up the turn tables in a corner. Soon, the room was rocking to old Studio One tunes and everyone was on their feet dancing, taking care to avoid the food.

"Special request for the beautiful birthday girl," Michael said. "Big up yuself Mum!" "Michael, you're a joker," Aunty Bliss said.

"Guilty as charged, Ma'am," Michael answered. "Taking you back in time with some authentic Studio One and Rock Steady beat... to bring out the sun and make you shake your hip and move your feet... yeah... Remember this one, Mum, from Prince Buster *Rude Bwoy Gyaan a Jail*... and I bet you remember this one: Toots and the Maytals, *Someone's Going To Bawl*? Noh watch that though, Mum. You're not doing any crying today no matter how hard the rain fall."

"Me and my husband, John Paul, used to dance to those when he was alive but I know I'm going to bawl later when mi bad knee start," Mum answered.

Michael grabbed hold of Mum and started dancing with her around the room.

"Behave yuself, Michael," Mum protested laughing. "I'm too old for all this."

"Really?" Michael asked, laughing as he twirled her around. "Wasn't it you that told us not so long ago that you're old but you're not cold?" Mum and everyone squealed with laughter.

Lolly got out the video camera and started filming. As I watched my family eating, dancing and laughing, I realised that these were very special "golden moments" as Michael calls them, to savour because as Mum said, life doesn't come with a guarantee and no-one could be sure they would be present at the next family gathering.

"A see yu can still drop some fancy foot work eh Mala?" Uncle Al shouted, doing some fancy footwork of his own in his striped socks. "Mind mi corn toe though; gwaan girl!"

"I know, Al. Never mind bad knee. You're not kidding me, Mum," Michael said. "I bet you still strut your stuff in front of the mirror when you think no-one's looking." Mum couldn't stop laughing as Michael spun her around again and her stocking feet skipped lightly across the carpet.

"Go Grandma! Go Grandma! It's yu birthday!" Lolly and Cousin Myra's daughter, Tiana (Tootsie) started chanting as they, joined in the dancing with some of the other young people. Old and new dance styles clashed on my living room floor and we had to push the food further into the corner to make room.

"Do some break dancing now, Grandma!" Lolly shouted as Michael changed the record and he and Mum started doing the twist.

"What about di dutty wine?" Tootsie shouted, giving us a demonstration.

"Never mind dutty wine, pull yu skirt down and behave yuself!" Cousin My shouted, slapping her on her gyrating bottom.

"No Tootsie, man, di migraine skank! Do the migraine skank, Grandma," Lolly shouted, holding her hands up to her head and dancing across the room.

"But Lord, yu see mi dying trial. Unnuh goh weh from mi! Break dancing mi foot bottom; move yuself! The only break dancing mi a goh do is probably break mi hip," Mum laughed, batting Lolly's hand away. Lolly neatly skipped out of range of the hand.

"Dad, show Grandma how to do the moon walk!" Shari who should have known better shouted.

"Michael can do the moon walk?" Aunty Bliss asked. In spite of herself she was on her feet too dancing.

"Yep," I replied proudly, trying to copy Lolly's migraine skank. "He certainly can; that's been his party piece for years."

"That's it, Mum, put your hands like this," Lolly encouraged. "Now do this."

"Mixer cyaan moonwalk to Toots and The Maytals, him noh dat good," Ferdie, my cousin Babsie's husband said, using Michael's nickname.

"Daddy can moonwalk to *anything*, Uncle Ferdie," Lolly answered before Michael could say anything. To prove the point, Michael took hold of Mum's hands and started doing the robotic backward slide across the room, made famous by Michael Jackson.

"Kiss mi neckback! Mixer must be di original rude bwoy Prince Buster singing 'bout fi true if him can moonwalk to a rock steady beat," Uncle Al cried. Michael just gave a bow and went to change the record as everyone applauded.

"Well Mixer, if I didn't see it wid mi own eyes a wouldn't believe it," Ferdie chuckled. "Yu better noh start holding up yu trousers front though or Aunty Mala wi beat yu."

"Mixer," Uncle Al said, "you and Mala should audition for *Britain's Got Talent*. Me and Ferdie will be your backing dancers, noh true Ferdie?"

"Yeah Man!" Ferdie replied. Out of breath from dancing, he got himself a red stripe beer and a chicken drumstick and settled himself on a large bean bag. "Wi can goh drop some foot fi Simon Cowell. Show dem yoot ya wid dem trousers a drop off how fi dance," he said pointedly as he looked at Richie, his teenage son. Richie smiled and pulled up his drooping jeans over his stripped boxer shorts which were clearly visible.

"Bwoy, this is the life," Ferdie added as he took another bite of his chicken and stretched out with his arms behind his head. "Now mi know how di Romans dem did feel when dem have dem banquet. Hey slave girl!" he shouted to Babsie. "Come and feed me one a dem juicy looking patties over deh soh." Laughing, Babsie entered into the spirit and went to sit next to him with a couple of patties on a plate.

"Yu facey devil; I'll give you slave girl," she said, breaking off a piece of soft crumbling pastry and playfully stuffing it into Ferdie's open mouth.

Lounging on the floor was certainly different and much more fun than we expected as the adults in my family rediscovered their inner child on a stormy Saturday afternoon. My grandson, Issy and my brother JJ's children, found it very amusing to see the adults occupying an area which was usually their domain.

"I love the rain," Cousin Myra said as she relaxed against the wall with a plate full of food and her feet up on a cushion.

"Me too," Cousin Babsie said stretching out next to Ferdie.

"Hey, that's not fair, Babsie," Ferdie protested. "How come yu a eat di two patty dem? You're supposed to be feeding me."

"Hush man. Mi did get dem fi yu but dem ya salt fish patty too nice fi share. A Cousin Myra mek dem. Yu know the best night's rest I've ever had Cousin My is when I've been soothed to sleep by heavy rain beating on the window," Babsie said.

"What about when me sooth yu to sleep?" Ferdie asked, trying to snatch a piece of patty from Babsie's plate.

"Sooth what?" Babsie said, pushing him away and hunching over her plate to protect her patties. "All yu ever do is toss and turn, pull the quilt off mi an' keep me awake wid yu snoring."

"A must be some other man yu a sleep wid a night time because mi know seh mi noh snore," Ferdie answered, kissing his teeth. "Lolly, bring Uncle two a dem patty deh, baby."

"You're right about water being soothing. When I was having Issy," Shari said, "some of the women in my anti natal class were having water births."

"Water births!" Cousin Babsie cried. "Lawd have mercy! I thought the idea was to get a new born baby to breath air not drown it as soon as it's born."

"Three quarters of National Health Service Hospitals provide water birth facilities in hospitals and at home," Aunty Bliss who is a nurse said. "They're very popular these days."

"I wanted a water birth but the date Issy was due was already fully booked," Shari said. "My midwife told us that it's less stressful for a baby and less painful for the mother to give birth in warm water."

"Well I suppose that makes sense," Babsie agreed, "because a baby develops in fluid for nine months where it's cushioned from light and loud sounds so it must lessen the shock of suddenly finding itself in a bright and noisy world."

"Di poor little mite dem; no wonder dem scream when dem born," Cousin Myra said. "When yu born, if yu did know what yu know when yu turn big, yu would turn and go right back into the womb."

"Uuh?" Shari said as we all looked puzzled at Cousin Myra.

"Did you know that without water there would be no life at all on this planet?" Lolly asked.

"Yep, that's for sure. H_2O – we'd be dead without it." JJ said.

"What does H_2O stand for anyway?" Mum asked.

"That's the most common chemical formula that nearly everyone remembers. It just means water, Mum. You know how everything is made up of atoms, water is made up of one part hydrogen atom and two parts oxygen," JJ, the family professor, said.

"My little brain can't take in all that so yu better save it for yu classroom John Joseph," Mum said.

"It's interesting though Aunty Mala," Cousin Babsie said. "I like when JJ and Lolly tell us things. I could never understand any of dem t'ings at school but when JJ explain it, it mek sense!"

"Glad to be of service, Cousin Babs. Did you know that we're made up of sixty percent water?" JJ was on a roll now and there was no stopping him.

"Sixty percent water? Where yu get that nonsense from?" my mother asked sceptically.

"It's true. Well, men are sixty percent water anyway. Women are made up of about fifty-five percent water and babies as much as *seventy-five* percent." JJ continued.

"Now is how dem know dat? Yu cyaan pour somebody into a glass and measure dem," Mum said. "Dem waan give poor people all di money dem tek a waste fi find out stupidness."

"I'm not surprise baby have so much water," Uncle Al who was playing picture card snap with Issy said. "After dem peepy and bawl so much, dem must have some way fi get rid of all dat water deh. That's all my bwoy do for the first few weeks after him born, noh true Bliss... peepy and bawl. If you weren't mopping up one end, you were mopping up the other."

"Snap!" Issy shouted banging his card down and jumping onto the pile, scattering cards everywhere.

"That's not fair; I wasn't looking," Uncle Al protested. Grabbing hold of Issy, they started rolling about on the floor, play fighting.

"Yes, it figures that men have more water than women," Aunty Bliss said with a chuckle as she moved out of the way. "The extra five percent is on dem brain."

"Wha'ppen to yu Bliss, man? Why yu have fi do man so bad all di time?" Uncle Al asked. "Is must be because man bigger than woman or maybe because woman chat too much, the extra five percent of water evaporate outa dem mouth."

"Well dat noh mek noh sense or babies wouldn't have more water than everyone else," Aunty Bliss said, sarcastically.

"All I know is there is nothing more satisfying than a glass of water when yu thirsty or a nice shower or bath when you tired to make yu sleep like a baby," Cousin Myra cut in quickly to head off the threatening argument.

"Two of our favourite walks are in Chorlton Water Park along the banks of the River Mersey and up by the Commonwealth Stadium along the Ashton canal. It's so peaceful listening to the water and watching it flowing along," Michael said. I nodded agreement.

"Yu know, Jesus described Himself as the living water in John 7:37-38, and is true," Cousin Myra said quietly. "He said 'If anyone is thirsty, let him come to me and drink. Whoever believes in me, as the Scripture has said, streams of living water will flow from within him'." At the tone of Cousin My's voice, Mum turned from the window and looked thoughtfully at her.

"That's right My. George is a damn fool! I've never said this before yu know My but you've been through a lot in recent years with George going off and leaving you like that and bringing up Tiana on your own. I am really proud of the way you've stuck with the church. You always have an inspiring scripture for every occasion to encourage us. You keep it up, yu hear. Never give up telling us what is right and what is wrong." Cousin My looked embarrassed at the unexpected praise but smiled proudly as everyone nodded agreement. Aunty Bliss who is always teasing Cousin My, causing them to argue and fall out, went over and hugged My.

"Sister Mala right, Noh tek noh notice of the things I say sometimes okay. I don't mean it."

"I know," Cousin My replied, returning the hug. "Yu did always troublesome from yu likkle."

"Amen to dat!" Uncle Al said.

"Shut yu mout Al! Anybody a talk to yu?" Aunty Bliss answered. Mum cleared her throat.

"Bliss yu should count yu blessings and be more respectful to yu husband in front of the young ones and set dem a good example of how married people should behave," she said sternly. Aunty Bliss opened her mouth to say something but thought better of it when Mum looked at her sharply.

"Yes, Mam," was all she said. Mum turned to Uncle Al.

"Al, you're mi brother an' a love yu but yu can be a pain in the backside sometimes. Stop teasing Bliss yu hear mi. We're family and we should learn to live better with each other."

"A sorry yu hear, Al," Aunty Bliss said. Uncle Al seeing the crestfallen look on Aunty Bliss' face, walked over to her and sitting down put his arms around her.

"Is ah right, baby. Sister Mala right though; mi baddah yu too much sometimes. Mi sorry too an' mi know seh yu noh mean it," he said. "Yu bark worse dan yu bite, don't?"

"Mum come and have some of your cake. It's your birthday," I said going to the window where she had been standing for some time. There is something about significant milestone birthdays that makes you take stock of life, consider your mortality and relationships with people. I think my mother was having one of those moments. I put my arms around her and felt her bones as I hugged her frail little body which not so long ago had been strong and healthy.

"Mi ah right, Kelly. Mi tired after Michael fling mi round di room so much pon mi bad knee but mi enjoy it. Mi just watching the water rolling down the road. Look deh, it reach right up half way up the car tyre dem."

I looked at the road which resembled an angry swollen river with a puzzled frown. The kerb was no longer visible.

"The drains must be blocked for it to do that."

"Mi noh know what sweet yu neighbour Jill. A two time she run out inna di rain wid di baby," Mum said. "See har deh again."

"No... something must be wrong."

As I looked out, Jill ran past our window towards the front door. At that moment, the light hearted banter of my family was cut off by a scream. Having discovered that floors, however well cushioned, and bones over forty don't mix, Lolly had been despatched into the basement by the older heads to fetch more folding chairs. Her scream made us all jump. Michael and I collided as we tried to get through the door at the same time. There was a frantic knock at the front door.

"Daddy!" Lolly screamed again. "Come quick, the basement is flooded; there's water everywhere!"

As Michael ran into the kitchen and down the basement stairs where he had his den and office, I opened the door to Jill who was standing there soaking wet and breathless. Her baby on her hip had a worried frown on his face and gave a pathetic little whimper as water dribbled down his face from his hair which was pasted to his head.

"Kelly," Jill gasped, "... you need to check your basement! There's water rushing into ours. Mike at number three and two other houses are flooded. Can Michael come and help me?" Jill burst into tears.

"It's all right... it's all right. Don't worry," I said as I listened to the commotion now going on in my own basement.

"I can't get hold of Pete. There's no service on the mobile phone because of the storm I think," Jill sobbed. I turned to shout for my brother but he and Ferdie were already behind me putting on their shoes. Uncle Al and some of the others had already ran downstairs after Michael. Shari took the protesting baby from the distraught Jill, soothing him as she took him upstairs to dry him off while Jill, breathing her gratitude, ran back into the rain followed by JJ, Ferdie and a couple of others.

In the basement, we quickly packed the door with old towels and cushions which prevented any more water coming in. Those who hadn't gone next door to help Jill, formed a chain and carried upstairs all that we could but the damage was already done as the floor was covered in two inches of dirty water. With buckets and mops we eventually cleaned up the excess water and mud.

By the time we finished, the rain had stopped and the torrent on the road had seeped away, leaving behind large pools where the drains were and a muddy sludge on the pavement. We had got off lightly with just surface water seeping in under the door, Michael having fitted what he called a none-return valve weeks earlier to the basement drain. This thankfully had blocked the drain when they water stared flowing back. Our neighbour Jill and others had not been so lucky and the old Victorian drains unable to cope with the volume of water had backed up and flooded their basements to a depth of up to a foot in some cases.

Issy spotted the rainbow first, arching majestically across a watery sky illumined by the last rays of the setting sun. The children jumped up and down clapping their hands with glee as they sang *"Red and yellow and pink and green... purple and orange and blue. I can see a rainbow..."*

I don't think the rainbow gave my adult neighbours any comfort as we rolled up our sleeves, put on wellington boots and assisted in bailing out water while contemplating a growing pile of soggy belongings and envisaged stressful insurance claims.

That evening my grandson, Issy, asked me to draw a rainbow for him. He lay at my feet, his face a study in concentration, as he carefully traced the lines of the rainbow I'd just drawn for him.

"Listen to your heart... listen to your heart... and sing everything you feel. I can sing a rainbow, sing a rainbow, sing a rainbow too," Issy sang softly as he coloured his rainbow.

I had forgotten that was how the rest of the words of the Rainbow Song went. Perhaps that rainbow was a sign of hope after all. We just needed to listen to what it was saying with our hearts.

After two days the laminate flooring in our basement began to lift and we took it up and dumped it in the skip with all our other now useless belongings. Several rubbish skips sat outside other properties rapidly filling up with ruined household items.

Michael took the disruption to his den and office philosophically.

"Could have been worse, babes. Could have been worse," he said with a shrug as we put his favourite easy chair, which had soaked up the stagnant water like a sponge, onto the skip. "I've wanted one of those fancy reclining leather ones for ages," he added.

Fortunately most things in the basement had been on shelves off the floor so the greatest casualty was the flooring. After wondering around the house for days looking lost and getting under my feet, Michael claimed the dining room as his temporary office and personal space.

We endured weeks of noisy industrial dehumidifiers and heaters drying out the damp floors and walls before we could redecorate and the insurance company graciously paid up.

Although Jill and Pete, our neighbours had much more water in their basement than we did, unlike ours, their basement had not been converted into usable living space. Once we helped them to bail out the water and it was sprayed with disinfectant by their insurance company it dried out with no lasting damage.

Before the flood, my neighbours and I went about our separate businesses, caught up in our busy lives with a perfunctory nod or cheery hello from a distance but with no time to stop for a real conversation. I didn't even know the names of most of them. After the flood, having all mucked in to help each other, everyone on our avenue became friends, developing a bond born of the shared misery of seeing our water logged homes which ensure that we now stop and enquire how each other are when we meet. We share portions of our lives now, giving invitations to family events.

Mum says every disappointment is a blessing if we would only open our eyes to see it. Perhaps it's our minds we need to open. In spite of the rain and the flood, Mum had a wonderful birthday and we enjoyed our indoor picnic. If we hadn't been at home, the damage to our house would have been far worse. If we hadn't had the flood, my neighbours and I would have continued living our separate lives, nodding and smiling at each other from a distance.

"We just don't realise how lucky we are you know, Kelly," my neighbour Jill remarked as we sat in my house drinking coffee recently. We were watching the misery of the victims of the latest floods in Pakistan on the news, with new empathic eyes.

"We don't Jill," I said, swallowing the lump in my throat as I saw the look of hopelessness on the faces of some of the women. My mum is right, we really should count our blessings. Unlike those poor people, when we were flooded, no lives were lost and we had insurance and the means to replace our things that were damaged.

What happened to us could in no way compare to the floods in Pakistan and more recently in places like the West Indies which suffered wide scale destruction and death by water. Our experience, however, made my neighbours and I dig deep in our pockets to give to the flood relief.

Thank you God for the experiences in our lives which make us a little more humane. On this occasion it enabled us to stretch out a compassionate hand to our brothers in their hour of need.

6 Walking The Walk

It has been my belief for some time that religion serves a vital function in society that it is no longer serving on a large scale. You only have to look around at current social problems to see that there is a need for organised religion and its guiding principles, whether that takes the form of church, mosque, temple or shrine according to individual beliefs.

If I had been a fly on the wall of my Cousin Myra's house last week Sunday after church, I would have needed a few aspirins to get me through the afternoon and the raging debate that took place.

Like most other black families, my family's spirituality can be plotted on a scale from confirmed atheists to every Sabbath and Wednesday night prayer meeting fervent believers. Among the believers are Muslims, Seventh Day Sabbath keepers, Jehovah's Witnesses, and a variety of denominations of Sunday worshippers. We therefore had quite a mixed bag when Cousin Myra invited us all to her church to hear her preach for the first time, after proudly passing her Lay Preacher's course.

Some of us went more willingly than others. I was surprise to see certain family members who to my knowledge hadn't set foot in church for years, until I remembered just how persuasive my cousin could be especially on God's behalf. I found out later that Cousin Myra's invitation had in some cases been packaged in bribery (dinner at her house afterwards with her famous rum-less rum cake for dessert). Others had been accompanied by veiled threats such as, '*next time a phone yu maddah in Jamaica a might have to mention that girl yu spending yu money on why yu cyaan afford fi fix di roof pon har house.*'

Whenever my extended family are under one roof, fortunately not too often, you can bet your life an interesting debate will result on some current topic or other and sparks will fly. I've learnt over the years to have a fire bucket at the ready in the form of soothing, diplomatic words to cool hot tempers.

During the first half of dinner as we shifted enough food to feed an army, we exhausted the topic of Dudus, the so called Jamaican drugs Baron and the recent events in Tivoli Gardens. Of course everyone had an opinion on drug trafficking, the CIA, the Jamaican government, lawyers and loopholes.

The debate moved on to the usefulness of churches in modern society when someone asked what role, if any, the church had played in the proceedings to resolve the problems in Tivoli Gardens. Cousin Myra got annoyed.

"Why when t'ings go wrong in people life whether dem believe in God or not, dem calling out God's name and want to point the finger of blame?" she asked.

"Mi dear Ma," my mother answered. "Like seh when dem did a carry on wid dem badness dem didn't know the Ten Commandments."

"Exactly! Dem treat God like insurance. Is only when disaster strike dem a turn di house upside down a look fi di policy," Cousin My said. "Chuh!"

"An' when it noh pay out dem blame God, when dem noh did read di small print in di first place," my Uncle Al added, laughing. Everyone laughed except Mum and Cousin My.

"Al, a keep telling yu 'bout yu joke dem yu know," Cousin My said. "This is not a laughing matter."

"Well you started it," Uncle Al protested, still laughing. "I was only trying to help you out."

"If someone was feeding me and paying for my children to go to school when no-one else is doing it," my brother John Joseph (known to us as JJ) said, "I'd defend them too. Pass the rice please."

"It's easy to talk John Joseph when we don't know the full story but two wrongs don't make a right," Mum said. "Yu want plantain?"

Mum produced a plastic container from her bag which was big enough to hold food for at least five people.

"Put likkle food ina this fi mi Myra den mi noh have fi cook tomorrow," she said. Without batting an eyelid, Cousin My took the container and started spooning food into it.

"Give me three piece of fish, My, because mi invite mi fren fi come fi dinner and she might bring fi har fren," Mum added. Laura (Lolly), my youngest daughter who had come home from university for the weekend, and I looked at each other with raised eyebrows. I smiled and Lolly burst out laughing. Mum looked at the two of us seriously.

"A wah wrong wid yu?" she asked as Cousin My dutifully put the requested three pieces of fish, rice and vegetables in the container. Is it only in a black Jamaican family that this could happen, I wondered?

Dishes clinked as people helped themselves to food. With a mouthfull of chicken and the bit between his teeth, JJ continued that if the government of any country wasn't helping poor people then they had the right to help themselves.

"All the churches are stuck in the Middle Ages. They have no vision that's why they haven't evolved," he said.

"How church fi have vision and evolve?" Mum asked. "Their job is to teach people how to get to the Kingdom."

"Change to meet people's needs, Mum" JJ said patiently. "People have changed but most churches haven't. Uncle Ferdie pass the dumplings."

The general feeling among the family was that JJ was right. The importance of churches in the lives of people had changed significantly in recent decades. From being the focal point of society, churches along with Christianity in Britain had been sidelined to almost a nonexistent role in most people's lives.

"They cyaan pull the wool over poor people eyes anymore since we learned to read. We know too much," Ferdie, my cousin Babsie's husband, said.

"Not just poor people, *black people*," Uncle Al said. "Dem cyaan use religion fi control us anymore. Every black man, woman and daag yu meet these days read somet'ing somewhere and questioning somet'ing."

"But that's *good*, Uncle Al; they need to," JJ said. "Black people have been held back by lack of knowledge or false information for too long." Mum sighed heavily.

"John Joseph, why yu have to come wid yu revolutionary talk on the Sabbath?" she asked.

"It's not revolutionary talk, Mum and the people taking advantage of us don't take a day off. We live in a world where it's survival of the fittest."

"Yeah man, JJ right, "Ferdie said. "Preach it yoot. We can't just sit down and accept we are poor and powerless. We need a vision for the future."

"That's right, baby, but some people need fi tek off dem dark glasses so dem can see fi eat dem food first, don't?" Cousin Babsie said pulling Ferdie's shades off.

"I'm all for change but it's not everyt'ing yu must run goh pick up, JJ. We need to be careful we don't throw out the baby with the bathwater," Cousin My said."

"These days the bathwater is so dirty you can't see the baby. It's time to fight for our rights," JJ said.

"Why men want to fight all the time? What's wrong with just sitting down peacefully and working things out? Yu ever hear of any woman declaring war on anyone?" Mum asked.

"Only dem husband," Uncle Al laughed, ducking as Aunty Bliss, his wife, threw a bread roll at him. "A Eve start all dis when she did bite di apple in di Garden of Eden yu know."

"Well Adam didn't have to tek him fool fool self goh follow har yu noh," Cousin Babsie said.

"Because man noh have no sense, Babsie, an' that's the problem," Mum said.

"That's okay, Mum," JJ chuckled. "We can handle whatever you throw at us, can't we Uncle Al? That's why men's shoulders are broader than women's?"

As he had a habit of doing when something tickled him, Uncle Al snapped his fingers like he was spurring on a horse.

"Aaay! See it deh!" he shouted. "Gwaan my yoot! Because dem outnumber us dem think seh dem can bully us." JJ and Ferdie nodded agreement. Mum just looked at them and kissed her teeth.

"See what I mean, Babsie – no sense," she said. "Unnuh broad shoulder is to carry unnuh big empty head." Mum and Cousin Babsie burst out laughing and raised their hands to exchange a high five.

Cousin My looked sideways at Lolly.

"Some people, especially young people don't believe in the Bible anymore because they think they're too educated, noh true Lolly?"

"No Cousin My, it's because we don't know *what* or who to believe anymore. We ask questions and no-one seems to know the real answers. Black historians are telling us now that everything we've been taught is based on lies."

"Yep! The Egyptians had the answers all along," JJ said.

"Well, I believe everything I read in my Bible is true not stories from Egyptian pyramids," Cousin My answered emphatically.

"You have to admit it's all a bit confusing though, Aunty My," Lolly replied.

"Well I'm certainly confused," Ferdie said. "I can't get mi head round all the 'thees and 'thous' in the Bible. If yu find me a Bible weh seh 'Dem' and 'Unnuh' mi wi read it."

"Uncle Ferdie, there isn't a patois Bible so you'll just have to buy a modern English version," JJ said. "The evidence the historians are talking about is there for anyone to check for themself, like I'm doing, Lolly. You have access to books and the internet if you really want the truth. It's true most of what we know doesn't add up but the truth is out there," JJ said.

"*The truth is out there*! Lolly said in a deep echoing voice which made everyone laugh.

"Nobody these days, not even the ministers, really understand why we on this earth. Dem all searching an' just as confused as the rest of us yu hear Lolly," Cousin Babsie who could always be relied upon to be controversial said. She paused examining her long painted finger nails while she chewed noisily on a chicken bone. "See, this is the way I see it. Maybe we knew once, a long time ago. Then because certain people wanted to hide the truth, we lost the knowledge. Every now and then somebody come up wid a new theory about God. Somebody else add to that, then dem write a new book and call it God's inspired word and run gaan wid it. After a few hundred years pass nobody noh remember what's lie and what's true."

"Speak for yourself, Babsie," Cousin My said. "My Bible tell me plain and straight that it's the inspired word of God. My God is the Alpha and the Omega... The Beginning and the End. Mi noh need fi know nothing more!"

"Yu mean di Bible dem copy from Egyptian story?" Ferdie asked, mischievously winking at Uncle Al.

"Now look 'ere, Ferdie! Don't come wid dat nonsense!" Cousin My shouted.

"Yu wouldn't know di truth if it bite yu pon yu nose!" Ferdie shouted back.

"Okay! Just calm down both of you!" Mum shouted. "There's enough religious wars going on already widout you two starting yu own!"

Cousin My folded her arms crossly and she and Ferdie glared across the room at each other with narrowed eyes. Ferdie started flexing his hands in a mock Egyptian dance but Cousin My just ignored him. Babsie dug him hard in his ribs with her elbow.

"Behave yuself!" she hissed. "Yu an' Al worse than di pickney dem."

"Why you lot have fi have opinion on everything when it cause so much argument?" Mum asked.

"Mala if yu don't have an opinion yu dead an' even duppy have opinion," Uncle Al said.

"Don't make things worse, Al," Aunty Bliss said impatiently. "How can duppy have opinion when dem dead?"

Cousin My looked up from her dinner. "The Bible says in Ecclesiastics 9 verse 5 that the dead know nothing," she said.

"Hmm! The dead know nothing? Yu stay deh. Yu mek duppy tek set pon yu and see if dem noh know nut'n. Dem know how fi frighten di living day lights out of yu when dem come widout dem head and start *whoooo*!"

"Al! "Aunty Bliss said sharply, "Shut up an' eat yu dinner before yu frighten the pickney dem wid yu nonsense!"

"It's not nonsense," Uncle Al insisted. If yu ask me, di duppy dem might as well gwaan ina di half empty church dem goh sid dung an' full up pew."

"What good would that do dem when dem dead?" Cousin Babsie asked.

"Well some church nowadays is nothing more than a social club so dem might as well goh socialise to, noh true Ferdie?" Uncle Al asked.

"Yeah man," Ferdie answered. "Is like fashion parade every week a Myra church – wid clothes and shoes to match hat and handbag. Every Sunday dem dress like is wedding dem going to. Mi nah wear my one old suit goh run competition wid anybody just fi mek Myra pastor throw word pon mi." Cousin Myra kissed her teeth.

"Why unnuh deh pon poor Myra soh today?" Mum asked.

"A Satan," Myra answered. "Don't worry yourself about me yu hear Miss Mala. When somebody know God, dem know how fi keep dem peace when foolishness a chat a dem ears. Pastor Smilie not troubling a soul. The poor man just preaching his sermon. It must be your conscience bothering you Ferdie when Pastor hit the nail on the head. All I can say is, if the cap fits..."

"Well if it's shoes and matching handbag you need to go to church Uncle Ferdie, I'm sure Grandma will lend you one of hers," Lolly laughed.

"Some a dem dress til dem too posh fi carry Bible and hymn book in dem hand," Uncle Al continued. "Dem all carry briefcase fi look good and me an' yu know seh is only last week church bulletin, one handkerchief and maybe one apple dem have in it."

"An' di Saturday church dem even worse!" Ferdie cut in. "You would think the queen herself was visiting."

"So why you two think your good clothes is called your Sunday best?" Cousin My asked. "Because you *should* wear your best clothes to go into God's house not to go an wine up yuself and party. So you think it's ok to dress up for the Queen but not for the King of Kings?"

"Of course you should give God your best but it's not God dem doing it for - it's all for show Cousin Myra," Uncle Al said.

"How you know that when you hardly go to church?" Mum asked. "Is how many people you ever ask why dem goh to church?"

"Me noh need fi ask anyone Mala. I work wid some Christians and you can't tell them different from anybody else especially when rude joke a tell. Dem laugh louder than everybody else. Mi holier than most of dem weh seh dem a Christian."

"Well I'm not judging anyone," Cousin My said. "The Bible say let him who is without sin cast the first stone. Which part of you holy or is without sin when the only time you call on Jesus or God is when you cussing."

"If you ask me the church need to look after all dem lonely woman deh weh siddung depressed a cry ina pew. Any man goh ina your church Myra better take him body guard or one of the woman dem might lick him ina him head like in caveman days and drag him off to har house. Come to think of it maybe that's why there are more women than men in the world. Di church woman dem must have dem lock up ina dem house."

Cousin My was smiling as she shook her head.

"Al, what is wrong with you today? Why don't you stop talking rubbish!"

"You just don't like to hear the truth, Myra, man. The single men in your church are either under age or have one foot in the grave. If any single man under 100 join the church it's handbags and high heels at dawn. Yu better move out of the way fast yu know Ferdie, or you get trampled in the rush for a wedding ring."

Cousin My was laughing now along with everyone else.

"The church might not be perfect but you can't let that stop you from going. The Bible says the wheat and tares have to grow together and only God can see the heart so only He knows who is who."

"I'm not against church yu know Myra," Uncle Al said. "You know we were all brought up in church. The principles of the Bible are good ones to live by but what the church doing about all the single women in the community with sons without a father around to set them a good example."

"The church full of boys who *won't* hear and old men who *can't* hear," Cousin Babsie said, laughing.

"Hmmm... so you think the church should do more for single women with children Al?" Cousin My asked thoughtfully.

"Definitely!" Uncle Al answered.

"You think so too, Ferdie?"

"Yeah Man, mi agree wid Al, noh true JJ?" My brother nodded.

"I've always said that the church needs to do more to support the young men in our community because they are our future," he answered.

All the women had suddenly gone very quiet as they listened.

"Ok, gentlemen, I'm going to give you a chance to walk the walk as well as talk the talk," Cousin My answered. The men suddenly saw the danger but too late as Cousin My reeled them in.

"It just so happens that Pastor Smilie, you know the one who keeps throwing word at you, Ferdie, is looking for some mature family men to organise a young men's mentoring group – mainly to support the single mother's in the community, Al... with their sons, JJ. You three shining examples of good fathers would be perfect. So see you next Thursday evening at church 7.00pm *sharp!*"

My brother, Uncle and cousin were speechless. The fly on the wall must have been laughing his head off. I know all we women were.

7 The Mentoring Group

Ferdie kissed his teeth as he blew on his cold hands and dug them deep into his pockets.

"It's all your fault yu noh," he said crossly. "Al, when will you learn to keep your big mouth shut, man! Why yu goh trouble Myra an' har church? Why?"

"Ah sorry man, ah sorry but it wasn't mi one. Yu an' JJ did your share of talking too." My Uncle Al pulled up his collar and snuggled into his thick coat.

"Ah right, yeah mi know; we all equally to blame. Where's JJ anyway? Myra said 7.00pm sharp an' mi noh wan' she lash mi wid har tongue. The woman tongue sharp like razor."

Uncle Al and his best friend, Ferdie, my cousin Babsie's husband, picked their way carefully down the uneven icy path that led to the front door of the old church. I followed equally carefully. All was quiet and gloomy, the atmosphere leant sombreness by the dark evening.

The grand old building with its sturdy buttresses, ornate carvings and mock marble pillars had seen better days. Its once beautiful stained glass windows, depicting familiar favourite scenes from the Bible, had long been replaced with unremarkable frosted glass, protected by black iron grills. On both sides of the path, the rose bushes, severely pruned back for the winter protruded from the tilled soil, stark and bare. Like the soil they were coated in a thin dusting of snow as they waited patiently for the quickening of spring.

Like Uncle Al and Ferdie, I felt compelled to lower my voice. Once we stepped through the rusting wrought iron gates, the high ever green hedge which surrounded the church, made it seem as if we had stepped into a time warp, leaving the noisy rush hour traffic and harsh street lighting outside. The peaceful hush which commanded reverence made me feel that a few transparent figures floating in the air across the lawn with its still fountain would not be out of place. Only frosty emptiness came from the screaming mouths of the gargoyles which should have been spewing water.

Memories came flooding back as our footsteps crunched on the path which had been newly sprinkled with rock salt and sand to prevent accidents on the ice. The church was like a grand old lady in the community – one of the few landmarks still remaining from the sixties when I had first come to Britain. Uncle Al never got tired of telling us how much he had loved church in Jamaica and his disappointment in the churches he had found in England. Church in Jamaica had been a welcoming, lively and friendly place but he hadn't felt very welcomed here initially and the service had been boring and lifeless. The ethnic make-up of the congregation had been different then too... mainly white. He had gradually become disillusioned with church over the years and with work and family commitments rarely attended these days.

Both Uncle Al and Ferdie had been married and had their children Christened here by Pastor Smilie's processor, Pastor McLennan. The old Scottish minister who had died five years earlier aged ninety-two had been posted to Manchester shortly after his ordination as a young man in the late fifties. In the same way many West Indians had held on to their accents, he had retained his strong Scottish accent to the end.

Pastor McLennon had often commented on how the ethnic make-up of the church had gradually changed over the years from mainly English to a variety of Caribbean and African worshippers who had brought a new energy into the church with their rich culture and lively worship. I remember him saying that the old hymns sung from the heart by West Indians had taken on new and vibrant meaning for him. He had spent several years in the seventies on missionary work in Africa.

On his return to Britain, Pastor McLennon could have had his pick of the choicest appointments but to the surprise of his fellow ministers, he had specifically requested to be returned to the Church of God in Moss Side.

The local community had a lot of respect for Pastor Smilie, whom everyone still referred to as the new minister, in spite of him being in post over five years. He was hard working and dedicated to his calling but times had changed dramatically from when Pastor McLennon was appointed minister to when Pastor Smilie took up his post. I felt a little sorry for Pastor Smilie sometimes. In fact I felt sorry for any minister of the church these days. They had a daunting task to shepherd today's wayward flock. I didn't know how Pastor Smilie managed to remain so cheerful all the time without letting his trademark gleaming smile slip or losing his now well-known habit of constantly saying, "Praise the Lord!"

The Church of God on Birley Street was sitting on prime land near one of the major routes into the city centre but as a National Heritage listed building, it couldn't be demolished. It could, however, be developed and turned into flats or remodelled for some other commercial purpose. The offers to buy from the City Council had stopped with the recent government cutbacks but they were still coming in from developers far and wide.

"The job of a minister must feel a bit like King Canute trying to hold back the tide – a real voice crying in the wilderness to all those empty pews every week," Ferdie said as if reading my mind.

"Noh baddah start get sentimental, man," Uncle Al said. "Dem want send di dyamn pickney dem goh a Jamaica fi a month goh get few licks fi fix dem business. This is the plan, cause mi noh have time fi mentor noh hard ears pickney."

"Yeah, yeah, man. Mi agree. Times hard and mi noh know how much longer mi a goh have a job so mi have to do any likkle over time mi can get. Mi noh have noh time fi it either."

"Right, that's settled. JJ have sense cause him noh even baddah fi turn up. We not even going in, yu hear Ferdie?"

"Yeah, man. Mi cool."

"But Uncle – " I started to protest but he silenced me with a look.

"Wi just a goh tell Pastor straight that we too busy. We cyaan do it, right?" my Uncle said.

"Yeah, man but what about Cousin Myra? She a goh kill us when she find out and any part a mi she noh kill, mi wife wi finish off. If she ina church already and she see us, she not going to listen. She just a goh pull us in and tell us fi shut up." With raised eyebrows, I looked at them both without saying anything.

"A dat mi a seh to," Uncle Al said with a worried look on his face."But no man! Look yah, wi is big man! We just have to stand up to Myra." Ferdie didn't look convinced but he nodded as we got near to the front door.

"Er... Ah right, you stand up to har and mi wi stand right behind yu."

As Ferdie stretched out his hand to open the door, it was thrown open from the inside and the path was flooded with a golden glow like a spotlight from the open door.

"Hello gentlemen! There you are! Good evening Sister Kelly. Come in!" Pastor Smilie stepped forward with outstretched hand and his trademark beaming smile – white teeth glistening in his thin tired looking face. The warm greeting and the hearty handshake took the two men by surprise.

"Good evening Pastor," I said, stepping into the hallway out of the cold.

"Er... evening Pastor," Ferdie said, hesitating on the step as he shook Pastor Smilie's hand.

"Evening Pastor," Uncle Al said also offering his hand.

Pastor Smilie looked up the path beyond the two men.

"Er... only two of you?" he asked. "Where is Brother John Joseph?"

"Oh... er... he'll he along soon Pastor... probably battling his way through the traffic, but Pastor - " Uncle Al said.

"Well, never mind gentlemen. Come in, come in out of the cold; follow me. We've all been waiting eagerly."

"Er.. Pastor..." Uncle Al said.

Pastor Smilie turned briskly on his heels and walked away down the corridor, leaving Uncle Al and Ferdie looking at each other with no option but to enter the building.

"Why didn't you tell him, man!" Ferdie hissed.

"Yu was nearer to him. Why didn't you tell him!" Uncle Al whispered back as they followed Pastor Smilie down the cheerfully painted corridor with its paintings of different religious scenes from the Bible. I followed trying to suppress my smile.

We were all at the church for the first meeting of Pastor Smilie's Youth Mentoring Group, at the invitation of our cousin, Myra. I had been invited to go along to represent *B All U Can Be*, the community project for which I worked as a volunteer counsellor. Before Pastor Smilie opened the double doors to the church hall, we could hear the soothing tinkling of the keys of a piano, vying with the rhythmic beat of drums, intermingled with the buzz of conversations and the laughter of playing children. As the doors swung shut behind us, with an air of authority, Pastor Smilie clapped his hands twice and cleared his throat to get everyone's attention.

The activities in the room ceased in a wave from the nearest people to Pastor Smilie, who began to make 'schee... schee...' noises. This was passed on with people nudging their companions until everyone except the drummer with earphones on and his head down, noticed the latest arrivals. All eyes turned towards us as the activities and conversations ceased. The drummer, sensing that something was happening, looked up and stopped drumming in mid beat. Embarrassed, he hurriedly removed his headphones, which slipped from his grasp and clattered noisily to the wooden floor.

"Sorry Pastor," he said smiling sheepishly.

Uncle Al was suddenly pushed from behind as my brother JJ, out of breath, crashed through the doors. Pastor Smilie turned, smiling with extended hand.

"Ah... Brother John Joseph, there you are, just in time. Praise the Lord!"

"Sorry Uncle. Good evening Pastor. Sorry I'm late; got caught in the rush hour traffic."

"Not to worry Brother John Joseph. Glad you could make it. Now we are all here we can begin." Pastor Smilie clapped his hands again.

"Take your seats everyone, please... quickly now!"

The buzz of conversations, shuffling feet and scraping chairs mingled as people settled themselves. Pastor Smilie led the way onto the platform, followed by Cousin Myra who was, smiling nervously. I recognised the two Community Police Officers, Phil and Darren from Cousin Babsie's birthday party. The two officers sat on the platform, giving a convincing performance of being relaxed in a situation that was out of the ordinary line of duty. Only their eyes gave them away.

We looked out onto an almost full hall. On the front row were a number of young people trying to look 'cool' but not being as convincing as the two police officers, as their eyes looked from each other to the floor. I recognised members of the group *Mothers Against Violence*, sitting with members of the newly formed group *Fathers Against Violence*. There were also members of the Street Pastor Team present.

"Bwoy, Pastor Smilie really mean business with this group," Ferdie whispered.

"Shut up man," Uncle Al whispered back crossly, kissing his teeth. "Wi could be at home now having a beer." Cousin My glanced at them out of the corner of her eye.

After praying, Pastor Smilie welcomed everyone and introduced the people on the platform. As well as the local police and probation service, there were representatives from various community groups and local schools.

"Our special guests this evening, Ladies and Gentlemen, praise the

Lord, are these three fine,upstanding fathers of the community who are going to be our parent mentors. Praise the Lord!" The three men smiled hesitantly, not quite comfortable in their new found fame. A few people, including Cousin Myra, shouted, "Amen!"

"First we need to look at what you feel the needs of the community are," Pastor Smilie said. "We have invited some of our local families to come and tell us. So at this point I'd like to open up the floor to you for your comments."

There were murmurs as everyone looked at each other. A young man stood to his feet, hesitantly. He said that he had come to the meeting to support his mother because of his fourteen year old brother who was in a gang. He had reasoned with his brother and pointed certain things out to him. His brother now wanted to leave the gang but was frightened of reprisals so he needed support to do it. There was applause as he sat down again.

Then a young woman stood up and said she was there because as a single parent she needed some help and advice with her son, a sixteen year old who was bullying her because he thought he was the man of the house. She began to cry as she described how her son came in and out of her house with his friends at all hours of the day and night as he felt like it. He was rude to her and to her family and friends who tried to speak to him. He hadn't been able to get a job since leaving school and didn't seem to have any interest in looking for one.

The young man who had first spoken put his hand up again.

"Before we say any more, Pastor, I just want to know if everything we say is going to be reported back to the Five O... er... sorry... police, by the two ...er...gentlemen there... the community police officers. 'Cos my mum wants my little brother to get some help, not get thrown into jail."

Pastor Smilie thanked him and assured him that no-one wanted that and that PC Warren and PC Nesbitt themselves would address those concerns when they spoke about exactly what they would be doing in the group and whether there would be a conflict of interest between their roles.

A single father bringing up his daughter alone spoke next. He had come along for support, he said, after she had told him that she was pregnant. He felt he had failed her and wanted some of the older women in the church to befriend her and give her advice.

One by one people stood up and said why they were there, with bent shoulders weighed down with care, some had to pause, choked with emotion as they spoke. I watched Pastor Smilie as he listened keenly, assuring each person who had spoken as the applause died down that they had come to the right place and he would ensure they got the help and support that they needed. If not from the mentoring group then he would help them to access other organisations.

"The government aren't fooling anyone, blaming black people in Moss Side and our kids for everything," A woman shouted. "It wasn't our kids who were rioting and mashing up and looting the city centre last week!" She waved a copy of the *Peace Week* news paper and continued that she liked the idea of the new Outstanding Social Behaviour Award to encourage positive behaviour. She and her family had decided this year to support the community by taking part in The Family Lantern Parade for Peace and her kids had loved it. There was loud applause and nods of approval as she sat down again.

The mentoring group meeting went on for some time with many issues being raised and decisions made as to exactly how the group would function.

"I'm telling you Uncle Al, I feel really bad you know after hearing all that this evening," JJ said as the meeting ended and we came off the platform for refreshments. "I have to admit that I only came to tell Pastor Smilie and Cousin Myra that I don't have the time to help to run this group but now I feel I have to. The mentoring group is really needed and I can't let these people down. I know most of these kids and their parents."

Uncle Al and Ferdie who were busy helping themselves from a plate piled high with slices of sweet potato pudding, looked at each other.

"Gwaan noh Ferdie," Uncle Al said.

"No, man yu tell him."

"You know JJ I have to admit, me and Ferdie came here for the same reason," Uncle Al said, clearing his throat. "We was going to back out too but I feel I definitely can't now; ah feel real bad."

"Well seeing you both confessing," Ferdie said sheepishly, "I guess I might as well come clean. I wasn't even going to come here tonight but Babsie, told me not to bother coming home if I didn't. I'm not sure what she meant when she said she not giving Cousin Myra any money."

"Oh there you all are," Cousin Myra said coming up. "I am so proud of the three of you but I have a little confession to make and I'm really sorry. I must admit, I was so sure none of you would show up that I...er... had a little bet with Cousin Babsie, so I owe you an apology. You see now how much we need this group? I'm really looking forward to starting our first session next week."

"Yeah, me too Myra. It's going to be good. I'm kinda glad now that you bullied us into it. I like the sound of the communication skills training *Be All You Can Be* are going to run, Kelly, and the outreach project Pastor Smilie will be in charge of to go and talk to people in their homes."

"Yeah and because JJ teach some of these young people, they know him and trust him already. What did that little guy say? Yeah, that you 'safe' JJ but he's going to keep an eye on the Babylon for a while before he trusts them."

"It's a good thing Phil and Darren understand that the young people see them as police first and mentors second and they will have to work at getting their trust," JJ said.

"You got that right, Granddad," the young man who had first spoken said, coming up to us. "We've got our eyes on all of you."

"Less of the granddad you; I remember you now Tyrone Brown. I used to teach you at Birley High School."

"That means you really are ancient then. So what do you want us to call you? I'm not calling you Mr McKenzie. I'm not at school anymore." A second youth came up.

"Just call them The Three Musketeers, Guy – Al, Ferdie and JJ...wicked! That's what my dad used to call them. You went to Birley High School with my dad didn't you JJ and you used to play football with him on Sunday mornings... before... before my dad... died." My brother was stopped in his tracks.

"You're never Mike Swift's lad... Jordan isn't it? You've grown! I'm really sorry about what happened to your dad. How are you doing? How's your mum?"

"I'm all right. Mum's ok too but I've been... er... getting into a bit of trouble recently that's why she made me come tonight. I wasn't gonna come back next week but I might now. Wait till I tell my mum who's running our mentoring group. Sick!"

Confession is good for the soul, so they say, so I have to admit that I too had tried to think of an excuse why I couldn't get involved in the Mentoring Group. That was until I remembered a young man with a handsome crooked smile, whom I had counselled at the *Be All You Can Be* Project. He had introduced himself to us only as John Smith and had talked to me about his harsh upbringing which had led him into a life of crime and prison. I had attended his funeral a few months before. He had turned out to be the leader of a notorious gang in the area and had been shot dead by a rival gang. If I could help Pastor Smilie and The Mentoring Group to save the life of one John or Jane Smith in the community then my time would have been well spent. I thanked God for Cousin Myra and Pastor Smilie and was really glad I made the effort to go to the meeting.

8 The Value of Obedience

It's funny how we don't appreciate the value of obedience until we are old or in trouble. As children we have to take the word of adults that they know best until painful experience teaches us that they really do, on most occasions. In the same way our fore parents, Adam and Eve had to learn the hard way that God knew best.

I've got a large scar in the middle of my left leg, a little below my knee. It's a strange shape sitting a bit lopsidedly in the middle of my leg like a flattened light brown leech with a life of its own. My scar has grown up with me – my constant companion despite being subjected to many home made concoctions in my teenage years of salt and lemon juice, baking soda and honey, and various over the counter fading creams. I've left it alone partly because I gave up pretending that I have mini skirt legs and partly because of my daughter, Shari.

The first time Shari noticed my scar, she was about *three* years old and we were at the supermarket.

"What's that?" she asked in the loud voice children save for public places like doctors crowded waiting rooms and even more crowded supermarket queues. To my embarrassment, the people nearby went quiet and all eyes in the queue followed her pointing finger to my leg.

"It's a scar, Sweetie. I fell and hurt it when I was about your age," I whispered, bending down towards her in an attempt to exclude the eaves droppers.

"Oh…. Poor leg!" Shari cried throwing her arms wide with a dramatic gesture that was worthy of an Oscar. "My poor Mummy! Let me kiss it better."

Before I could stop her, she threw her arms around my leg planted the noisiest kiss I'd ever heard on my scar and then proceeded to gently stroke my leg. I was overcome with emotion. Riddled with embarrassment, I smiled at the other shoppers and gently tried to prise Shari off my leg. There wasn't a face in the queue that didn't have a broad smile on it.

Now my scar is as much a part of me as my eyes and nose and I think I'd miss it if it wasn't there. Passing time has given me other scars, but that one is my favourite because we've been through a lot together. I suppose you could call that one my rite of passage to 'country'. I was born in Kingston, Jamaica because that was where my mother lived at the time.

My mother was 'sent for' and left me with my grandmother in Portland to go to England. I don't remember being consulted about my mother going or about living with my grandmother.

"Consult? Consult you 'bout what?" my mother asked as I sat in my kitchen with her, my Aunt Beverley, known as Bliss and my cousin Myra. "You were three!"

At that moment my partner, Michael, popped his head around the door.

"Are you lot arguing again?" he asked.

"Dem noh have nut'n better fi do," I heard my Uncle Al mumble in the hallway.

"Yu hear anybody in here a argue, Myra?" Aunty Bliss, his wife, asked as she grated cabbage for coleslaw.

"No Sah," Cousin My answered, lifting the lid off the steaming pot of rice n peas and flaking up the grains with a fork.

"Mmm... something smells nice. We're off to the West Indian Centre for a beer and a quick game of dominoes," Michael added. My mother kissed her teeth.

"Unnuh too idle. Yu t'ink *we* noh have nut'n better fi do? Dinner is at 5.00pm so mek sure unnuh back in time or unnuh in trouble," she said.

"Michael, a beg yu ask mi husband fi pick up two bottle a wine for dinner from ASDA when yu coming back, cos mi nah talk to him," Auntie Bliss said. Michael turned and relayed the message.

"Mixer," Uncle Al replied from the hall, using Michael's nick name, "a beg yu ask my wife what kind a wine she want because mi nah talk to har either."

Aunty Bliss kissed her teeth.

"Mala," she complained to my mother, "is over thirty years mi married to yu brother yu know and mi just finding out how out a order him is." Out in the hallway we heard Uncle Al making the same complaint to Michael.

"My yoot, is nearly thirty years mi married to yu aunt yu know an' mi just a find out how damn miserable she is. Wha' kind a wine she seh she want?"

Mum rolled her eyes and turned back to me.

"When I was leaving Jamaica, I told you I was going away to get money to buy nice things for you," she continued, "and that you were going to live with Mama for a little while. What more did you need to know?"

"Those days are not like now, Kelly," my Cousin Myra said. "It wasn't the West Indian way to ask children's opinion on anything."

"Yu dead right and it still isn't," Aunty Bliss, said. "Some parents nowadays mek mi laugh. Dem discuss every blessed t'ing wid likkle pickney and confuse and distress di poor t'ing dem. A big people fi mek decision not pickney."

"But I think children *should* be asked their opinion, Bliss," Cousin Myra said "Pastor Smilie said it's good for their psychological development."

"Well I don't know 'bout dat but yes, you should give them a choice sometimes but parents should have the final say, noh true Sister Mala?" Aunty Bliss winked at Mum and did a classic Jamaican quick pout of her mouth in the direction of Cousin Myra when My wasn't looking. We all knew that Cousin Myra had no control at all over her teenage daughter, Tiana (Tootsie to us).

"Yes," Mum agreed. "Some parents don't set any boundaries..." Mum stopped when she noticed Aunty Bliss pointing and nodding towards Cousin Myra who had her back to us. Mum flicked a tea towel at Aunty Bliss's pointing finger and gave her a hard stare as she realised what she had been drawn into.

"And those same parents," Aunty Bliss continued, "are then surprise when dem pickney, age eighteen going on eighty, feel seh dem have di right to run dem own life, noh true Myra?" Cousin My turned around with a puzzled expression. She looked from Aunty Bliss who was smiling mischievously to Mum who was trying to smile innocently.

"Di chicken smell nice, Myra," Mum said kicking at Aunty Bliss under the table. I just looked at the three of them, shook my head and looked out of the window as I tried to keep a straight face.

"When you were leaving Jamaica, I remember arriving at Granny's house with all the bags and suitcases and everyone making a fuss of us," I said to change the subject.

"Do you remember getting the fish bone stuck in your throat when we were eating dinner?" Mum asked. "I'll never forget that as long as I live. Yu stop breathing and went limp. Mi frighten so til mi nearly wet up myself."

"Yes... I do remember. Someone turned me upside down and pushed their finger down my throat to get the bone out. That made me vomit, which dislodged the bone, thankfully. I don't remember who the 'someone' was though. Was it Granny?"

"Probably," Mum answered. "I don't remember either I was too hysterical. Mama done tell mi noh fi give yu di fish because it have too much bone. I was being stubborn, thinking... a fi mi pickney, I can give har fish if I want to. I think I was upset because I knew I'd be leaving you the next day." I couldn't imagine my calm, no nonsense mother being hysterical or deliberately disobeying my formidable grandmother, the matriarch of our family.

"I clearly remember the finger and the bone like a razor in my throat stopping my breath. I also remember screaming a lot."

"That's how I knew you were going to be all right because you were screaming so loud," Mum chuckled. "Yu were trying to pull your little dress down because yu didn't want anyone to see your underwear as yu Uncle Redman held you upside down trying to shake everything out of your mouth. Yu really remember all that when you were so young?"

"Mmm," I answered. "I do."

That's really strange, because I don't remember my mother actually leaving or being upset at being left. The brain in its attempt to protect us is very selective in what it remembers. I just remember she wasn't there but there were lots of people who were. They were there for hugs and kisses and to sooth me with sweet syrupy mangoes, tart ginnep and juicy stainy purple and green star apples, when I fell and grazed my knees or got stung by nettles or didn't like country food.

"Sister Mala yu kept that quiet. So yu nearly kill poor Kelly before yu left Jamaica because yu cyaan hear?" Aunt Bliss chuckled.

"Well yu can noh baddah talk," Mum said. "Is disobedience why yu picky picky head look like fowl a come from mango walk an' yu have fi wear wig." I held my breath, shocked at the insult but Aunty Bliss burst out laughing.

"Fowl a come from mango walk! Ha ha ha! I haven't heard that expression in a long time. Mama used to always say that, Myra."

"Yeah mi remember. Yu remember yu used to have tall, tall hair down yu back when yu was a teenager, Bliss?" Cousin My asked.

"Yeah man an' mi disobey Mama an' tek mi faas self goh mek mi fren, Suzette, put jerry curl ina it. It drop off clean an' never grow back good."

"But listen noh... give yu joke," Aunty Bliss continued. "The other day, the postman bring a parcel when I was getting dress. Missis a didn't know which one fi grab first, mi wig or mi skirt fi run goh open di door. Cos him always a admire mi hair and mi noh want him fi see seh a noh fi mi and mi cyaan open di door ina just mi blouse and underwear," Aunty Bliss laughed. Mum, Cousin Myra and I were laughing too.

"Soh wha' u do, Ma?" Cousin Myra asked.

"Wha' mi fi do Missis? Mi grab di wig an' fling it pon mi head and hold a towel in front of mi an' goh open di door. Wha'ppen to yu?" Aunty Bliss said.

"Mi tek di parcel and walk weh still holding di towel in front of mi. The only problem is wi have a glass panel in di front door and mi figet til mi turn round an' see di postman eye dem nearly popping outa him head soh mi just have fi run upstairs." We were all cracking up laughing now.

"But wait noh... is only when mi goh back upstairs mi realise seh mi put on di wig back to front."

"The post man probably didn't even realise Aunty," I said.

"Anyway mi sure seh him see whole heap worse than Bliss ina har panty," Mum said.

"Mi sure of that," Aunty Bliss said, "If he'd seen me without my wig then he really would have had a tale to tell."

As we laughed, my mind wondered back to my arrival at my grandmother's house in Portland. Not being used to 'bush' in such abundance, I spent my first weeks hiding behind Granny's long skirt in terror of plant and animal. I remember one day my cousin who wasn't much older than I, saying mockingly,

"Pssst... Likkle Kingston gal, wha'ppen to yu... yu 'fraid fi everyt'ing weh move?" But from that day I think he took pity on me and made it his job to educate me in the ways of country life, after enticing me from behind my grandmother's skirt with sugary coconut drops and grater cake.

Over the next few years, my cousin Orville (Chappy to us) with his torn shorts, who never had any buttons on his shirts or shoes on his feet, taught me the names of the plants, birds and insects. He taught me to climb trees and to shoot birds with a sling shot and was the reason for most of the scars I now have on my legs. Once the land had marked me, it claimed me and I was no longer afraid. I belonged to it and was accepted.

Shortly before I left Jamaica, Chappy was sent for by his parents who had left him with Granny and gone to the USA. He is now a successful grey haired business man who wears designer suits and speaks with an accent that sounds as if he was born in Miami.

As I got old enough to understand, I was told that my mother was in England. She might as well have been on the moon for all that meant to me. My grandmother would come back humming happily from the post office and say,

"Kelly yu maddah send money fi yu. Yu is a lucky likkle girl. Noh fret, she soon send fi yu, yu hear."

Sometimes a parcel would come from my mother or sometimes from one of our other relatives either in England or in America. My mother sent clothes, shoes and dolls with pink rubber skin, cherry red cupid bow lips and long shiny blond hair. I thought they were the most beautiful dolls I had ever seen and I was the envy of all my friends. Their dolls had been cut out of cloth, sown together by hand and stuffed with soft material before having faces drawn and carefully stitched on with coloured thread. I had a doll like that too and although publicly the foreign doll was my favourite, it was my hand stitched rag doll which I took to bed and cuddled close at night. She was the one I told my deepest fears and reprimanded when I was angry.

The scar on my leg is a reminder of my painful encounter with 'the baatroom spot', as it was called. I don't know exactly how old I was when I was ensnared by the bathroom spot.

My mother had a far away look in her eyes when I reminded her about the incident in the supermarket with Shari.

"The baatroom spot… yes I remember. It was joined onto our house at Mount Elias. Redman, yu Aunt Peach husband, was a builder. He was supposed to build a bathroom extension onto Mama house, to tek the place of di pit toilet cos it did full a lizard and one big old bull frog always a mek noise ina di bush by di doorway. Yu Aunt Peach did always have fi tek someone wid har every time she visit Mama an' wan' goh a toilet fi shake bush an' frighten dem weh. That's where you get it from."

"What?" I asked.

"Frighten fi every blessed t'ing. Mi noh know if sommady can frighten fi worm. Hee hee hee!"

I smiled but with a tinge of sadness as I remembered Aunt Peach and Uncle Redman who both died some time ago. I had seen their tombs on my last visit to Jamaica.

Redman wasn't my uncle's real name. I never knew what it was. None of our family were called by their real name and we still all have our 'pet' names today. We usually only find out someone's real name at their wedding or their funeral when everyone would half suffocate themselves trying not to laugh when the pastor read out the name. People would look at their neighbour and mouth,

"Yu lie! Him name wha'?" This was the case when my Great Uncle Zeb and Aunt Mary got married. The entire congregation was in uproar as we found out that Uncle Zeb was named after all twelve of the tribes of Israel.

One person in the family always let the side down and the laughter would splutter out through lips they were trying to keep shut tight – you know that stuttering uncontrollable laugh that makes your eyes water and makes you start to cough. Once one person in the family went, that would set off all the young people. Someone would always have to run out of the church, screaming with laughter. And the older people would be trying to look 'stush' – dignified to me and you, and give us 'the look' but it just didn't work because 'the look' of the Caribbean parent is a serious thing that adults can't give with a big smile on their faces no matter how much they try to cover their mouths with their hands.

The pastor would do a loud *"Ahem"* and that would bring most of us back to order. But again there was always one... the one who had to hide their face behind a handkerchief, dab their eyes and pretend they were really crying. That sort of thing was bad enough if it was a wedding but if it was a funeral it was a good idea to find out the persons real name before you go into church, have a good laugh and then put your funeral face back on.

I don't know if the bathroom had been my uncle's idea or if he had been coerced into it. Aunty Peach was good at coercion, but the foundation was laid and that was as far as it got. To my knowledge that was as far as it ever got.

On the day I arrived at Mount Elias, Granny saw me eying the strange concrete construction, and said, "Kelly, nuh go play round deh soh, yu hear. Yu wi fall down pon de baatroom spot."

I peered round the back of the house curiously. The evil looking concrete edges like shark's teeth, about six inches high around a smooth rectangular room size space didn't look like something I wanted to argue with. By the look of it, I guessed it had existed there in exactly that state a lot longer than I had. I had been taught from a very early age to obey my elders, so as a rule I kept well away from the bathroom spot but with the magnetism of the serpent in Eden it drew my attention.

It was all the fault of the sweetsop tree. It set a trap on behalf of the concrete and ambushed me – well, actually it was the fault of the *ripe* sweetsop the tree dropped there when it became too obese with sweet milky juice to cling to the tree any longer. It had surrendered its hold and committed suicide, breaking into two on the jagged concrete edge of the bathroom spot. Anyone who is familiar with sweetsop will know *'it sipple'* as Granny would say but slippery or not, it was irresistible to any child.

Did God really say if you eat of the fruit of this tree you shall surely die, Eve?
Did Granny really say if you go near the bathroom spot you will definitely fall, Kelly?

The ripe sweetsop lay there beckoning; it's creamy deliciousness like the fruit in the Garden of Eden. Funny how, with my belly full of sweetsop, I clearly remember catching my dress, stumbling and slipping as I tried to pull it free. I remember my leg connecting with the jagged edge of the concrete and my whole body being engulfed by intense pain which sucked the breath out of me. Then I was deafened by a scream. To this day I don't know if it came from me or one of my cousins. I did hear one of my cousins shout,

"Granny come quick, Kelly dead! She really dead fi true dis time, Mam!" just before darkness obscured the image of the sun blazing down on me and I lost consciousness. I've been told since what happened but I don't remember. I do know now the value of obedience.

As my cousin Myra who could always be relied upon to quote for us a suitable verse from the Bible to illustrate her point said, had I obeyed my grandmother I wouldn't have ended up with "dat big dutty scar weh spoil up yu leg."

"If Eve in the Garden of Eden had obeyed God, Kelly, mankind would not now be in the predicament that we find ourselves."

"Yes Cousin My," I answered.

"You know in Geneses 3 verse 3 the Bible says:

"But of the fruit of the tree which is in the midst of the garden, God hath said, Ye shall not eat of it, neither shall ye touch it, lest ye die."

"Yes Cousin My."

"And what happened when Eve ate the fruit, Kelly? I think we all know the story well don't we?

"Yes Cousin My."

Although I was left with a permanent scar, fortunately, my punishment for disobedience was not as tragic and far reaching as our fore parents. I did not die or bring death into the world but the pain was excruciating. I was told my leg was so badly injured that nothing Granny did would stop the bleeding and Uncle Redman had to rush me to hospital at Buff Bay in his car with Aunty Peach playing my mother's role, wailing hysterically in the back of the car about how she was going to break the news to Sister Mala that they had killed her one pickney.

I vaguely remember not being able to go to the local church school 'private school' which I loved, for a long time because I couldn't walk and I remember being carried around by one of my older cousins, Marvin (Vinney). I also remember Vinney taking me on more than one occasion on his bicycle to have my leg dressed at the hospital in Buff Bay. He would carry me on his back while he wheeled his bicycle up the track from our house and down the hill until we got to Cross Roads where there was a real road.

Once on the way back from the hospital we stopped, seeking shade from the blazing sun by one of the orange groves. The trees laden with fruit stretched out as far as the eye could see. Vinney leaned his bicycle up against the roadside bush and telling me to stay where I was, quickly disappeared, reappearing again minutes later with two green skinned oranges in his hand. He was already deftly peeling one with his little penknife, the skin curling around unbroken like a flattened green and white snake. We dug our teeth into the firm refreshing flesh of the sweet juicy oranges as we made our way up the steep, winding hill from Lennox to Black Hill, Vinney pushing his bicycle with me on his back. Having travelled that hill in a car recently, I concluded that my cousin who was just a teenager at the time, must have been extremely strong or I must not have weighed very much.

My mother sent letters which Granny read to me saying I should be a good girl and I would come to live with her soon. As the years went by and I didn't go to England, I would look at my scar guiltily, wondering if it was because of my disobedience why my mother had not sent for me. Years later when I found out the complex and varied reasons why my mother had been unable to send for me as quickly as she would have liked, that thought still lingered subconsciously. That was probably why I had made such efforts to get rid of my scar and the evidence of my wrong doing.

I only began to accept the value of the lesson I had learnt about obedience from my accident with the innocent acceptance of my scar by my daughter. The process of acceptance and forgiveness had only been completed on learning that my mother and my aunt whom I respected and admired for their wisdom had also had moments of disobedience with unfortunate consequences; me nearly losing my life by choking on a fish bone and my aunt permanently damaging her beautiful hair.

Years later when I visited Jamaica, I didn't even recognise where our house had been because it was so overgrown – the bush had reclaimed its own but the concrete foundation of the bathroom spot, green with moss now, and the sweetsop tree, gnarled and twisted, were still there. I gave both a wide berth.

The Jamaican countryside is a wonderful but dangerous place for an inquisitive little town child. British children – and I mean the black ones too, don't know how lucky they are, or on reflection maybe we are the fortunate ones. They have beautiful unblemished arms and legs that I still envy but we, the children who weren't born in Britain, have real life experiences that are priceless. I don't know one single child who spent their early years in Jamaica who hasn't got a sizable scar or three on their legs mainly knees and ankles but other areas too, legacies of 'the sore foot'.

'The sore foot' is a testimony to the harsher side of the beautiful Jamaican landscape which as children we often came into closer, more painful, contact with than we wanted to, with the words of an adult echoing in our ears,

"Chile yu too disobedient! If yu cyaan hear, yu wi feel!"

If you think it's only the blood of slaves or soldiers on the soil of Jamaica, think again because every child who was born there has given a pint or two along with the skin off their knees and elbows as well as the top of both their big toes. Lord, the pain of bucking your big toe; especially if you dislodge the toe nail! As my Cousin Myra says, mankind is surely paying the price of disobedience now as the earth soaks up our blood and tears.

Today I learnt another vital lesson from my extended family. Even though we may still have to endure the consequences of disobedience, we should take something positive from the lesson. It is important to forgive and ask for forgiveness but it is equally important to forgive ourselves and not carry around the burden of guilt or shame for past actions and allow it to blight our entire lives.

9 Letter To Michelle

In recent years, I have come to the conclusion that should any budding anthropologists out there want to do an interesting study on human behaviour, I will nominate my extended family. They would make a fascinating study. Any psychologists who want to make a name for themself can also apply. They could call the study *"The Jamaican Under A Microscope."* It's possible that it's been done already, but my family would present some interesting new insights. They are one of the most interesting bunch I have ever come across. Some people would say eccentric, others would just say... strange.

Recently, my cousin Barbara (Babsie) and I were summoned to my mother's house, to help her spring clean. On our arrival, Mum had the vacuum cleaner and step ladder ready plus a box full of assorted cleaning equipment, some of which had long past its use by date. The request was to help but my mother supplied refreshments, directed operations like a seasoned general and didn't lift a finger the whole time Babsie and I cleaned.

"Aunty Mala, why yu spring cleaning in di middle of summer? A t'ink di clue is in di name – *spring cleaning.*"

"Anybody know when is spring, summer, autumn or winter in this blessed upside down country, Barbara?" Mum asked. "Yu noh see we get all four seasons sometimes in one day. Sun a shine, breeze a blow and snow a fall hard."

"Mmmm, I suppose so," Babsie admitted. "And di house an' di vacuum cleaner don't know if it's spring or summer."

"Yu could clean in winter and call it spring cleaning," Mum said, trying to chisel floor polish from a tin that had hardened to the consistency of stone. I didn't comment because I could see the conversation descending to a place from which it would be difficult to pull it back.

When Mum felt she had given us enough instructions, that we could be trusted to be left alone to do the job to her satisfaction, with a glass of home-made ginger beer and the *Gleaner* newspaper tucked under her arm, she retired to relax in the garden and –

"Tek a likkle sun in mi old bones for di arthritis."

All went well until Cousin Babsie started sorting through a bag of old bills and assorted papers mum had given her. Sitting in the middle of the living room floor, Babsie started to chuckle, then to laugh out loud. I turned from my perch on the step ladder, dusting the curtain rails to look at her.

"Oh my Lord!" Babsie cried suddenly.

"What?" I asked curiously.

"Oh my good Lord!" Babsie exclaimed again. "She didn't!"

"Babsie, what!" I asked again, quickly descending the ladder for a closer look at the letter she held in her hand.

"Lord bless us and save us, but yu maddah noh easy. Kelly listen to this," Babsie said, looking up at me with a broad grin.

Now before I go any further, perhaps this would be a good time to tell you that in January 2009, my family and I, at my mother's insistence, went to Washington DC to witness for ourselves, the inauguration of the first black president of the United States, Barack Obama. My mother said, and we all agreed, that it was a significant historical occasion that we would never again see in our lifetime. She added that as head of our family in England, it was her duty to ensure that we saw it with our own eyes, not read about it or see it on television because, she said, "dem could an mek it up an' tell lie 'cause mi never hear noh black man wid dat deh name deh."

We had called a family conference with the usual mammoth cook out of all foods Jamaican, music and dominoes. I had then been despatched to the travel agents in Chorlton, accompanied by my mother, to purchase airline tickets for ten family members.

As my cousin Babsie began to read the letter aloud, I now peered at the beautiful handwriting, almost like calligraphy script, which my mother prides herself on having been taught as a young girl at school in Jamaica.

*** *** ***

Dear Michelle,

I hope when these few lines reach yu they will find yu and Barack and di likkle gal pickney dem well. I had to write yu dis letter fi let yu know I was there on di 20th January last year in the crowd at Barack's inauguration. Yu couldn't see mi, I know, but I was di one waving the Jamaican flag and holding di picture of Mr Bruce Golding... nice man. A buy a pair of binoculars 'specially so a could get a good look at yu dress. Yu an' di girls dem look nice in yu colourful clothes. Di big girl look like a blueberry and di likkle one look just like a tangerine. Unnuh really bring some colour to di White House.

Mi sorry it tek mi soh long fi write but mi kinda have a busy year wid di mad people dem weh me call family.

Mi an mi daughter, Kelly and mi big son John Joseph and all di rest of di family was there on Capitol Hill. We got a special deal from Miss Lou's Travel Agents, di one in Chorlton just by the fish man. Him sell nice fish but if yu ever goh there, don't buy di chicken cause it noh did look soh fresh last time mi in there. Anyway, di flight took us to New York and mi did glad 'cause mi get fi link up wid some of di family weh mi noh see for dis long while. We got di Greyhound bus to Washington. I was fretting a bit but it didn't trouble mi bad back too much even though di journey tek three hours. Bwoy it did cold yu see Michelle, even though di sun was shining soh mi did glad fi see seh yu act sensible and dress up warm in yu nice yellow suit.

I was so happy when I hear dat Barack mek it. Mi have fi run goh tell all mi English neighbours dem seh Black man ina di White House. Praise di Lord! But 44th President? I don't know why it tek dem soh long. Never mind, it still nice an'

Barack happy. Missis what a way him can smile? Tell him it tek us hundreds of years to get there soh a beg him noh baddah gwaan wid noh nonsense and spoil it fi di rest of us who still a try. Tell him is now him really have fi goh watch him back. Make sure Barack wear his vest all the time... I mean di bullet proof one.

Di 21 gun salute nearly mek mi wet up miself cause mi did think seh a bomb a goh off. A few people near mi bawl out and fling demself pon di ground 'til dem realise wha' gwaan an' get up back shame, an' a dust off. One likkle fool fool bwoy start pop style an' a doh press up like seh dat a wha' him fling himself down deh fi do. Idiot! Wha'appen to dem people deh sah wid di big gun dem when dem a bawl 'bout terrorism an' a baddah people wid security. Dem mek mi even have fi tek off mi shoes at di airport. Mi was so embarrassed 'cause di cross eye security woman was looking at mi corn toe. Come to think of it maybe a noh mi toe she did a look pon at all.

Mi see yu an' Barack a hold hand and yu look sweet, baby. Noh pay noh mind to what dem bad mind people deh saying 'bout yu bottom, yu hear. Dem just jealous cause yours natural and yu noh need noh injection. Mi notice yu wearing yu skirt dem a nice respectable length but just watch dem dibby dibby gal deh wid dem legs weh reach up to dem armpit. All mi have fi say is... remember Monica Lewensky... nuff said.

Noh worry yuself 'bout dem Republican deh. When dem a try find skeleton ina cupboard a hope duppy tek set pon dem. God wi deal wid dem in Him own good time and rebuke dem just like Jesus rebuke Satan. Praise de Lord! By di way, Michelle ... I hope yu remember to put di Lord first in everyt'ing yu do.

Don't worry about cooking real soul food in the White House kitchen 'cause most white people like black food now. Yu waan see di queue outa Kool Runnings a day time and yu cyaan even get ina Chicken Run or Dougy's at all these days. Just remember fi crack di window a likkle when yu browning di chicken or yu cooking salt fish. When a seh crack, I don't mean break yu know, because yu know certain people t'ink wi aggressive already an' have chip on wi shoulder. I mean just open it a likkle fi let out di smell but not enough fi let in any teef or terrorist.

Don't worry too much about di security guard dem in di White House... after dem see yu tek off yu hair for di first time... dem wi get over it. Just put on yu tie head. Noh baddah gwaan stush and noh tie yu head a night time or wear yu stocking foot and mek yu hair drop off. Remember wi is black women and a soh wi do it. Yu cyaan walk round di White House wid noh picky picky head... no sah.

Remember seh some white folk get frighten easy especially when dem see more than three black people together and you, Barack and di pickney dem mek a crowd already so dem might want to stop yu in di corridor and search yu. I t'ink dem call it 'SUSS'. Don't let that stop yu inviting all yu relations dem round fi dinner from time to time or dem might t'ink seh now yu mek it yu noh wan' know dem noh more. Just remind any a dem weh tool up or like a smoke fi leave it at home. Tell dem noh tek it deh! Remind dem too not fi try fi sell anybody a second hand Rolex or anyt'ing even if dem still have di receipt.

On a different note, when it come to di cleaning, yu can let di helper do it but I'd clean di toilet myself if I were you as yu cyaan be too careful.

Don't be afraid to clap di pickney dem backside if dem get outa order but don't let mi daughter Kelly know seh mi tell yu soh cause she noh believe in beating pickney at all. She just lucky fi har two turn out all right. Anyway yu pickney dem look like nice likkle girls but pickney these days easy fi spoil like rotten pear soh yu have to watch dem good.

Anyway Michelle I must close now because di van come fi mi fi tek mi to The African Caribbean Care Group for di Elderly and mi noh waan miss di bingo cause first prize today is a bottle of Tonic Wine. Take good care of yuself and if yu ever in England, pass by Manchester and pop in for a nice cup of tea an' a slice a bun an' cheese. Give mi a bit of notice though soh mi can invite di neighbours round fi come shake yu hand.

I am yours most truly and sincerely
Grandma Mala

P.S: Dahling please excuse mi handwriting if it look a bit like crab toe. Is on account of di arthritis in mi fingers, especially ina di right hand. Is from when mi di did work at dat cold factory and hav fi walk ina di snow every morning goh ketch bus. If yu ever want fi tek on a good case, yu being a lawyer an all, yu can help mi get some compensation from di ol' devil dem, as long as yu noh charge mi too much. Yu can ask Barack fi help yu 'cause him look like a nice kind bwoy who wi give a old lady a bly."

***   ***   ***

As Babsie finished reading, we looked at each other... stunned and burst out laughing. The cough behind us made us jump. We hadn't noticed that Mum had come into the room behind us.

"Bwoy a soh unnuh faas. Wha' yu troubling mi letter fah?" she asked with a little mischievous smile on her face.

"Mum, this is a photocopy. Please tell me you didn't actually send this letter to Michelle Obama," I said, chuckling.

"And what if a did? That's between me and Michelle. Put it down and mind yu business."

Whether my mother posted the letter or not, she's not saying. We've no way of knowing if it was ever received. I'd like to think that it was received and at best made Mrs Obama smile. The thought of America's first lady taking domestic advice from my mother fills me with a great sense of pride. The story of the letter got around the family so a few weeks ago when the American President and his wife visited the United Kingdom, more than a few of us were waiting in anticipation of a call from mum to come and help her slice bun and cheese for Michelle.

10 Size Matters

Well 2010 was certainly a year to remember. It came and went so fast that as I sat and listened to the chimes of Big Ben, at Westminster, watched the spectacular firework display illumine the night sky, the London Eye and the River Thames in London, bringing in 2011, I wondered if it would be as eventful.

Various family members, as usual, have fallen out during the year, but we've made up and each time we do, the bonds between us seem to strengthen, making me realise in these uncertain times how important family ties are. We don't get to choose our family but, the old familiar saying rings true, blood is definitely thicker than water. Whether family members are loving, lazy or loathsome, you're stuck with them. For me they come through every time. I've come to the realisation that instead of trying to change my family to fit in with me, and Lord have a tried to over the years, sometimes it's for me to change to accommodate their little eccentricities because the benefits are priceless.

I am not one for making New Year's resolutions these days, simply because I've learnt with experience and hindsight that by the end of January, they usually lay broken and bleeding on the ground. This year, however, with my mother's increasingly pointed remarks about my weight and feeling as if I need oxygen every time I attempt to run up a flight of stairs, I decided something needed to be done. I say 'attempt' to run up a flight of stairs, because I'm usually wheezing, my knees having given up by the time I reach half way. The problem is, deciding something needs to be done, and actually doing it are two very different things. So let me tell you how I progressed from 'A' to 'B'.

After making friends with our two community police officers, Darren and Phil at my cousin Babsie's 50th birthday party, my mother was recently invited to Darren's baby's Christening. She had bought Darren's wife, Anna, a copy of Levi Roots' *Reggae Cookbook* for Christmas. Mum has converted all of Darren's family to West Indian food and was persuaded by Anna to cook curry goat for the party after the Christening.

After Darren delivered Mum's invitation, she was beaming from ear to ear.

"Oh he's such a nice bwoy," she said. "Him faadah is a detective in Liverpool yu know an' Anna is wid di mounted police. Mi used to see har ride pass all di time pon har big *arse* before she fell pregnant."

"Har big *arse*, Aunty Mala?" asked Babsie who was in one of her mischievous moods, grinning from ear to ear.

"*Horse*... I think she means ... '*big horse*'," I whispered, throwing a cushion at Babsie who burst out laughing.

"A wha' sweet yu now Babsie? Lawd yu can skin teet' een?" Mum said.

"Mi ahright, Aunty Mala," Babsie answered. "What yu going to wear to the Christening? You'll have to get a new dress an' get your hair done."

"No man, Kelly can put likkle dye ina mi hair front and straighten it fi mi. Mi have dat nice black dress she buy mi weh mi wear goh a church sometimes an' mi can wear mi likkle felt hat wid di pretty peacock feathers." Babsie and I looked at each other, horrified. We both knew the felt hat well.

"Mum, you don't mean that dress I bought for you about five years ago?"

"Yes, of course is it mi mean and it still look almost brand new. Mi wear it goh a funeral last week. Mi not like you, all my clothes still fit me. " I ignored the remark, even though it cut to the quick.

"Mum, you're not wearing that!" I said decisively.

So Cousin Babsie and I took my mother shopping. Never again! I think I may need therapy for a long time to help me get over the very traumatic experience.

We left home early, or what Babsie calls early, because I knew it was going to be a long day. Just how long I could not have imagined or I would have taken lunch, dinner and maybe a sleeping bag. I booked the morning off work but had to phone in and book the afternoon too, telling my manager that I had a family crisis. This wasn't a complete lie because by then, having spent over three hours with my mother and cousin, I was definitely in crisis.

"Oh... I see, " Alicia, my boss chuckled, sympathetically. "I forgot you were taking your mother shopping today. Good luck. Can I expect you in tomorrow?" Not seeing the joke, I pulled a face on the other end of the phone and assured her that I would be there.

I had no idea there were so many shops in Manchester, selling women's clothes. We started at The Manchester Arndale Shopping Centre, then drove down to The Trafford Centre, only leaving because the shops were closing, having bought... *nothing!* My mother had tried on countless dresses and found fault with every single one.

"Well is not my fault dem noh mek clothes like dem used to and you were rushing me," Mum said as we had a well needed cup of tea at her house. "I like di navy blue one mi try on in British Home Stores. That's the one I want." As expletives bounced around my head, I thanked God my mother couldn't read my mind. Not that I would ever dream of swearing at her. For a start, I like my teeth too much and picking them up one by one off the floor after she has boxed them out of my mouth is not a task which I fancy. Besides, I'm scared of blood, especially when it's mine and even more scared of pain. My mother is not a big woman but her right hand has had lots of pain inflicting practice over the years.

Babsie cleared her throat and shook her head at me before I could say anything. She knew as well as I did, that the navy blue dress had been the second dress which Mum had tried on in the very first shop that we had gone into! We had both told her how nice that dress looked and that she should buy it but she had found several reasons why it was not suitable. I took a deep breath and slowly counted to ten, something I've had a lot of practice at over the years.

"Okay, Mum, I'll go back and get it for you tomorrow morning before I go into work," I said with a forced smile that felt more like a grimace.

"I'll come with you and try it on again."

"Er... no Aunty," Babsie cut in quickly before I could let my tongue get me into trouble. "Tomorrow is my only other day off from work this week and you promised to come and help me sort out my garden... er before the weather changes again... remember?"

"I don't remember promising that," Mum said, "but all right. Yu know which dress don't yu Kelly?"

"Yes, Mum."

"An' yu know mi size?"

"Yes Mum."

Part of the problem was that, as our elders sometimes do, my mother had lost a bit of weight in recent years. "Old age shrinkage" Babsie calls. Mum was reluctant to accept this and insisted on trying on her old dress size, complaining bitterly that they must be putting the wrong labels in the dresses.

"Kelly, what a pity they don't do any of those nice dresses in your size; you'll have to go to the 'large ladies' shop. Hee hee hee!" It was remarks like that why I *gave up trying anything on after the first shop.*

"Yes that blue dress will goh nice wid mi felt hat," Mum added.

"Babsie," I whispered, when Mum took the cups into the kitchen, "I'll distract her while you hide the damn hat."

Having done her hair and applied a little make up just the way she likes it, when I dropped Mum off at the church for the Christening a few weeks later, she looked the business. She had a great time and hasn't stopped talking about it since, especially about the many compliments she got on her dress.

It was after the shopping trip with my mother and Cousin Babsie, that I made up my mind that the time had definitely come to do something about my weight.

"Is who seh we have to be a certain weight, height or skin colour fi look good anyway?" I asked Babsie, as we munched on salad and crisp bread, a few days later at my house. I knew it wasn't me and that was why I was cross with whoever it was who dictated to us what beauty is. Babsie looked at me. "Never mind," she said. "A tell yu what, if wi find out, mi wi hold him and yu can t'ump him back foot."

"Dis crisp bread noh taste bad yu noh?" she added reaching for another. I looked at her, then at the crisp bread that looked like grey sand paper, sprinkled with raisins to help the pretence that it's food, just to make sure we were eating the same thing.

"Are you kidding? It's like eating stale cardboard," I answered, as I munched out of the corner of my mouth, unenthusiastically.

My Cousin Babsie, bless her does not and has never had an ounce of spare flesh on her. Don't get me wrong, she's not thin. In my eyes, she has and has always had, even days after giving birth a toned, shapely figure that turns heads. My wonderful cousin, at her own insistence, was putting herself through what I saw as torture on my behalf, in order to support me in losing weight.

"Pass di salad. Dem wholemeal crisp bread 'ere nice man. Dem can eat," she said.

"How do you know it wasn't a woman who started all this nonsense about size?" I asked, looking at her curiously, wondering how anyone could actually like lettuce.

"No, I don't t'ink soh yu know, Kelly. Mind you, I could be wrong. Sometimes women can be the harshest critics of each other. Take Aunty Mala for instance. Is she why you have a complex 'bout yu weight, 'cause she always troubling yu. You ever hear Michael complain?"

I thought about it, and no, my partner Michael had never complained about my weight; in fact quite the opposite. The bigger I got, the more he seemed to take a shine to my bottom.

"You're right about women being worse for judging other women," I said. "We're the victims but the biggest perpetrators as well."

"Mmm... munch... munch..." Babsie said.

I have always been able to rely on my cousin Barbara for support on whatever venture I embark. On this occasion it was my latest low glycemic load diet. Babsie leafed through the booklet with a sceptical frown.

"Kelly, this low GL diet thing is just another fancy way of saying eating healthy low calorie foods, don't?"

"No!" I answered crossly. Babsie shrugged.

"Munch... munch... okay," she said.

My cousin and I have always been more like friends or sisters than just cousins, since I was left at my grandmother's house in Portland when my mother immigrated to England in the early sixties. Babsie too had been left in Granny's care. My cousin has had an unquenchable spirit of adventure and unswerving devotion to me from we were girls walking the bush of Mount Elias in Jamaica, stoning mangoes or following the boys to catch cray fish with their hand-made baskets in the babbling river below our little wooden house. The river gave us food, served as our bath and provided us with water for drinking and cooking. Further down where it ran wide and majestic, along a pebble and sand bank, the local women washed their clothes, scrubbing them on the smooth flat stones and hung them on bushes to dry. Bent double in the blazing sun, their skin of various shades of brown, shone with sweat, as dresses lapped between their legs and round bottoms in the air, they exchanged the latest gossip.

Even in those days, Babsie was usually up for anything no matter what trouble it might get us into. I had the ideas, Babsie helped me to execute the plan.

Mum says God short changed Babsie in the brain department so he had to compensate her in looks. I agree wholeheartedly about her looks but disagree strongly about the brain. Cousin Babsie just thinks differently to the rest of us in a very practical, straight forward way that nobody else would think of.

I needed to lose weight. My cousin did not, yet she was munching diet food with me as if it was the latest chocolate bar. Babsie is one of these people who eats like a horse, anything and everything and never puts on an ounce of weight. I love her dearly but, just between me and you, sometimes she makes me sick. I told her that one day during an argument. Her response was to look me up and down like a mother surveying a naughty child and say,

"Yes, but mi know yu still love mi and yu cyaan do without mi so shut yu mout." Put like that, I couldn't really argue.

As well as filling my fridge with salad and vegetables, Babsie signed us up for a year's membership at the gym of the local leisure centre, without telling me until we arrived in the car park. On the way back from our first session at the gym, feeling like I'd been trampled by a horse, I drove grumpily home, while Babsie bounced up and down in her seat to the music on the radio.

"Bwoy, I feel so full of energy!" she exclaimed.

"It's probably that drink you're drinking," I said looking at the blue and red can of soft drink in her hand. "Apparently it gives you wings," I added sarcastically, because it hadn't worked for me.

"I can't wait to get on that treadmill again and that rowing machine! I could actually feel it pulling my stomach in; look, look, doesn't it look flatter?" Babsie continued, ignoring me. I just felt depressed as I thought,

"Oh God, I can't do this again next week! Mi legs are gonna drop off."

I scowled as we passed a very slim woman with what could very easily have passed for a perfect body. She was dressed in skin tight shorts with matching trainers and cap and mincing effortlessly along the grass verge which separated the two sections of the dual carriage way on Princess Road. Now it has always perplexed me as to why if you are jogging to improve your health you would choose to jog alongside a busy road, and breathe in the exhaust fumes of hundreds of vehicles when there is a perfectly good local park. To actually run between two lines of heavy traffic was taking it to another level. I suppose there aren't as many people to see and admire your physique in the park where all the serious joggers with something to lose are running and wheezing around the pond, dressed in baggy jogging pants and even baggier t-shirts and scaring the long suffering ducks.

My cousin looked at me and as if reading my mind, she suddenly kissed her teeth, wound down the car window as I slowed down with the traffic and shouted,

"Go and sit your skinny arse down and eat a cream cake!"

"Babsie!" I shouted horrified. Put off her stride, the woman stumbled as she turned to see who had shouted. I just gripped the steering wheel tightly, willing the traffic to move faster as I looked straight ahead as innocently as I could but the dirty look which the woman gave us, told me that we had been rumbled. The woman gave us a finger gesture, recovered her stride and carried on running but with a less confident stride. Babsie burst out laughing and after elbowing her I had to join in.

"Barbara, you are terrible," I said.

"She's just showing off, Kelly man. Watch har noh; legs dem look like tooth pick."

"You've got room to talk; pot calling kettle," I said.

"Come on, Kelly, I know we've got maagah legs in our family but not that bad. Watch har noh, 'bout she a sport shorts when har leg dem look like twig… chuh!"

"Stop it!" I shouted, but I was laughing so much now I was just about keeping the car under control. The man in the car next to us did a double take at us and smiled. Babsie returned her best gold toothed smile, waved and winked at him. The man burst out laughing and shook his head. The traffic in front of me started to speed up and I pulled my shades down from on top of my head, hid behind them and drove off before my cousin could do anything else.

"Why yu want to lose weight Babsie? Yu look all right to me," my Aunty Bliss said, when we got to my Cousin Myra's house where we had all arranged to meet up for dinner. She cleared her throat and said nothing as she looked me up and down.

"Give me Kelly and Babsie chicken if dem noh want it Myra. Mi wi take it home for Al's dinner tomorrow 'cause mi working late. And if you could put a extra piece in for mi lunch, dat would be nice."

"Everybody waan change somet'ing 'bout demself," Uncle Al remarked. "Wha' Babsie have fi tek off when she already look like bone. Mi surprise yu daag noh bury har yet ina yu back yard, Ferdie."

"If Babsie tek off any weight, she have fi go back goh find it yu noh, 'cause mi noh like hug up bone a night time," Ferdie remarked.

"Di two a yu bald head favour bone," Babsie answered. "I don't want to tek off any weight; mi jus' a goh wid Kelly fi get fit."

"Fit fi what? Baddah people and give Ferdie trouble?" Uncle Al asked, winking at Ferdie with a big grin. Babsie gave him a dirty look. My mother looked up at both of them and cleared her throat.

"Fit fi t'ump yu ina yu pot belly," Babsie mouthed over mum's head.

"Kelly man, why are you listening to Mum? How many times must I tell you that you're not fat," my brother John Joseph (JJ) asked.

"Noh waste yu breath yu hear JJ," my partner Michael said. "You carry on eating your crisp bread, Kel. I'll just have a nice slice of hard dough bread every time."

"Society has a lot to answer for setting standards that people feel they have to kill themselves to live up to and be seen as normal", JJ said.

"You're right JJ. I tell you I'd like to give society a piece of my mind for causing us all so much grief," I answered.

"What you looking so annoyed about?" Uncle Al asked.

"It's not fair, Uncle. Who decides who or what is 'normal' and what gives them that right?" I asked crossly.

"It's simple; we do," my Uncle Al answered. "We're society."

"Mmmm...." JJ rubbed his chin and pondered. "Good question that,

Kel," he finally said. "I might use that one as a discussion topic with my Year Seven class."

"Al is right, Cousin My said, "we are society – the people, so we cause our own problems."

"But how? The way I see it, it seems it's the newspapers that run t'ings. They tell us what they want to tell us and how do we know any of it is true?" Babsie asked. We all pondered that for a while.

"Now there's another good question," JJ said. "I'm glad a came. That's my lesson plan for this week sorted. Is the media society's tool or is society the media's tool? What do you think then Cousin Babsie?"

"John Joseph, a want to eat mi dinner in peace; a beg yu don't start any of yu philosophical discussion at the dinner table and give me indigestion. What's wrong with discussing the weather like everybody else?" Mum asked.

"Kelly started it!" JJ protested.

"Liar!" I mouthed, laughing.

"Leave di yoot alone Mala, man; is a good question, kinda like a riddle," Uncle Al said.

"Never mind 'bout diet now, Kelly," Cousin Myra said. "Come eat your dinner yu hear." With the delicious aroma coming from the table, I didn't need telling twice.

With my cousin's help I lost seven pounds in a week. She didn't lose an ounce because what I found out later was that she ate salad and vegetables with me and then went home and ate her normal meals. As individuals we may be weak but where two or three are gathered, especially as a family, we are a force to reckon with. So does size matter? The answer is relative. It matters in some things and not in others, according to personal preference. I'll let my mother have the last word.

"My maddah used to say every hoe a dem 'tick a bush," Mum said. "If yu a giant, what yu a goh do wid midget?" This might be one for JJ's class to debate.

11 Praise Be

In the Bible, the Old Testament paints a picture of God as a powerful, jealous and vengeful God visiting the sins of the father upon the children unto the third and fourth generation. This prompted the need for Jesus, in the New Testament, to acquaint us with another side of God's character – a patient, long-suffering, benevolent Father with, in my opinion, a fantastic sense of humour. I know God must have a sense of humour or he would have wiped as all of the face of this earth a long time ago.

To be honest, listening to some people praying, my mother included, I think they are running a serious risk of being instantly struck by a thunder bolt from heaven every time they kneel down to pray. So, it's a good thing that God has a sense of humour and he is able to see the heart and not judge us by words alone.

A couple of weeks ago my mother was recovering from a bad cold and still coughing decided to miss church. I took my Bible and hymnal and decided to go round and keep church with her. As I got out of my car, My Cousin Myra pulled up behind me. She had decided to do the same thing and had collected my Cousin Babsie on the way.

The aroma of camphor, lavender and eucalyptus hung heavy on the air of my mother's house bringing back memories of my early years with my grandmother.

"If yu smell anyt'ing funny is mi cold remedy," Mum said as I sniffed the air.

"It doesn't smell funny - it smells nice," I said.

"Hmm... kinda warm and soothing, Aunty," Babsie added taking a deep breath.

Mum made us all fresh ginger tea with honey, to keep out the chill, she said and Cousin Myra had brought a pineapple cake with delicious lemon icing. The delicate china which Mum had insisted on getting out of the antique glass cabinet from the fifties, clinked musically against silver teaspoons. The cabinet was one of the first pieces of furniture she had bought on coming to England and had moved with her several times. The tea set had been one of her wedding presents.

"They're just sitting in di cabinet gathering dust 'cause everybody use mug these days," she said. "We don't entertain like we used to; everybody too busy."

"Is true Mala," Cousin My said. "Yu know is how many people have all these beautiful t'ings on display ina cabinet. The young people don't appreciate it. When yu die dem just give dem weh to charity shop."

All went well at first with our little gathering. While we ate Babsie entertained us with some jokes she'd heard on the radio earlier in the week.

"Cousin My," she asked. "Why was there no card playing on Noah's ark?"

"Babsie, will yu stop being daft. I don't know. Where do you get all this nonsense from?"

"Peace FM," she answered. "Yu know the new community radio station. The answer is, because Noah sat on the deck. Get it? Do you get it? You get it don't yu Kelly?"

"Er... no," I answered, hesitantly until realisation dawned. "Oh yes... because Noah *sat* on the deck."

"I don't get it," Mum said.

"Okay, listen to this one then Aunty Mala. Guess me this riddle and perhaps not. Where was Moses when he was smoking his pipe?"

"What yu mean where was Moses when he was smoking his pipe? How yu know Moses smoke pipe?" Mum asked. "Dem did have more sense in those days. Dem noh did smoke."

"No... no Aunty Mala man yu spoiling di joke... just answer."

"Well mi noh know," Mum answered, helping herself to another slice of cake. "Don't involve me in yu stupidness.

"He was behind the pipe!" Babsie shouted.

"Behind di pipe? What him was doing behind di pipe?" I started to laugh.

"Aunty Mala!" Babsie shouted. "That's the answer to the riddle! Where was Moses when he was smoking his pipe? He was behind the pipe!"

"Yeah ah right," Mum said. "Goh sid dung now an' keep yuself quiet."

We discussed the lesson for the week without falling out, looked up a few relevant verses from the Bible and sang some of our favourite hymns and choruses. We came a bit close to an argument a few times but Cousin Myra's diplomacy averted hostilities.

Cousin Myra suggested that Mum said the prayer to close.

I sat up straight in my chair and bowed my head. Cousin Babsie stayed as she was, stretched out in the armchair with her feet up on a footstool. Cousin My stood up and bowed her head, deliberately pushing Babsie's feet off the stool. Watching me out of the corner of her eye, my mother made a great show of fluffing up a cushion which she placed onto the floor to kneel on.

As I noted the preparation each one of us had made to pray it raised the question in my mind of whether there was really a wrong or right way to pray. I wondered if the positions we take when praying or the words, in some cases elaborate rituals and repetitive chanting, is more about us and our perception of reverence and respect rather than what God really wants from us. Is there really a right or wrong way to approach God if our prayers are genuinely from the heart?

"Aye... t'ank yu Jesus," Mum's words broke into my thoughts. She sighed heavily and I realised that she was looking at me disapprovingly.

"Soh wha'appen to yu?" she asked.

"Pardon?"

"Why you don't feel yu should kneel down and t'ank di Good Lord in di right and proper way fi yu blessings?"

"My knees are hurting," I answered. "I can't kneel down for very long."

"Yu waan get some exercise an' tek off some a dat weight. If a young, young woman like yu a bawl fi knee pain already wha' yu fi say 'bout mi? Jesus die on di cross fi yu an' yu cyaan bear a bit a pain fi him?"

Babsie must have been reading my mind because she answered before I could.

"Aunty Mala does it really matter?" she asked.

"Of course it matter!" Mum snapped. "It's about showing respect, Barbara! Would you stay sitting down, or lying down in your case, when yu speaking to the queen, especially if yu asking har fi some of har money?"

"No but God doesn't care 'bout things like that. Is only people mek all these rules and regulations to mek themself feel important. Is God mek the world an' Him already know seh wi just likkle insects and He's di King soh I figure whether wi stand up pon wi head or lie down pon wi face, as long as God know that we know He's boss, him cool wid dat."

"Babsie, what's wrong wid yu why yu have to be soh disrespectful all di time?" Mum asked.

"Leave har alone Mala, man. She jus' a express har opinion. Although mi noh soh sure 'bout dat yu know Babsie," Cousin My said. "God might know He's boss but respect is still due."

"Mum, you're such a bully," I complained as, feeling guilty, I knelt down, ignoring the pain. My right knee made an alarming creaking noise.

"Hee hee hee!," Mum laughed. "A really yu knee a cry soh? Poor t'ing… never mind but a bet if yu a walk outside an' yu see one £20 note yu'd an' bend down faas enough fi pick it up even if yu knee a cry eye water."

"Of course I would," I chuckled. Do you know how much £20 can buy in Aldi or Netto?"

"Yes mi love. Is dem a keep a lot a people breat' and body together. Yu goh ina di other supermarkets dem wid dem music and pretty light fi buy one loaf a bread an' one bakkle a milk an' come out wid two trolly full a buy-one-get-one-free somet'ing - t'ings weh yu noh even need an' weh goh bad before yu can use dem. Lawd, yu si wi dying trial? What a t'ing when yu eye dem bigger dan yu belly. Ah right Kelly, stop talk now man. Yu figet wi supposed to be praying."

"But..." I protested.

"How yu can talk soh much man? A don't know where she get it from Lord."

"Mum!"

"Hee hee hee!" she laughed mischievously. "Ah right... joke aside. Unnuh sekkle. Let's pray now."

"No, hold on a minute, Aunty Mala," Babsie said. "I have a question before we pray."

"Gwaan den noh," Mum said.

"Well di Bible say yu fi goh ina yu closet and pray in secret. How dat work if closet a cupboard? How somebody a goh pray ina cupboard unless dem tek out di shelf dem?"

Cousin Myra's eyes narrowed and she gave Babsie a serious look.

"Gal, but yu noh have noh sense," Mum said kissing her teeth. "It noh mean cupboard!"

"Are you trying to be funny again, Barbara?" Cousin My asked. "Mi did t'ink seh yu stop all this foolishness since mi ask Pastor Smilie to pray fi yu." For once I don't think poor Babsie was joking.

"No, Cousin My, honest," she answered looking embarrassed. "I've been studying di Bible yu give my Ferdie an' a dat mi read ina it but mi noh understand it. Mi did t'ink seh closet a toilet. Yu know like water closet? Dem just call it WC now. A Ferdie tell mi seh closet mean cupboard."

Cousin My's face softened and she looked as if she was trying hard not to laugh.

"A tease Ferdie a tease yu, Babsie," she said. "I know the scripture yu referring to – Matthew 6:5-9, don't?"

"Mi noh know, Aunty… mi cyaan remember now."

"Yes, is Matthew 6… here let mi read it." Cousin My turned the pages of her Bible.

"And when you pray, do not be like the hypocrites… but when you pray, enter into your closet and pray in secret… and when you pray, do not use vain repetitions… after this manner therefore, pray… Jesus was talking about the difference in the prayer of a hypocrite who prays in public or openly so that everyone can see them and someone with a pure heart who prays quietly just to God. A closet just means a private room Babsie, like yu bedroom."

"Oh…" Cousin Babsie said.

"Yu understand that now Babsie?" Mum asked.

"Yes, mam," Babsie answer.

"Ah right, Sister Mala," Cousin Myra said. "Gwaan pray now."

"No, hold on one minute while I just goh to di real water closet," Babsie chuckled, quickly leaving the room.

"Yu shouldn't rough har up soh, Mala, man," Cousin Myra whispered. "It's good she is studying di Bible an' I don't want yu to put har off. Yu know she like run joke an' she noh soh bright."

"Bright? Babsie is di original black blond. No wonder she like blond extension soh much. She is a blond woman in disguise."

"Leave har alone, man. Yu t'ink is little trouble mi have fi get har fi read di Bible. Is only because Richie nearly drown when we went on di trip to Wales that she and Ferdie start coming to church."

Babsie came back and we settled ourselves in a position to pray. Mum cleared her throat.

"Dear Lord is me again, Grandma M," she said. "Yes, I know yu know it's me Lord because yu must tired fi mi baddah yu. Well mi really sorry but mi have some fool fool people name family weh mi have fi put before yu before dem do anything stupid an' get demself ina trouble. And mi noh have noh money fi pay lawyer fi get anybody outa jail.

A beg yu touch di arthritis ina mi left knee weh a stop mi from bend down good cause it a bite mi like ants in deh. Noh baddah 'bout di other knee today 'cos it noh soh bad now since mi ask yu fi touch it last week.

T'ank yu for sending mi family fi worship with mi even though mi daughter like argue too much and t'ink she know more 'bout di bible dan mi weh a study it since salt fish a shingle house."

My mother paused, waiting for a response from me but Cousin My had a firm grip on my arm to remind me that Mum was supposed to be praying so I didn't say anything.

I half-opened my eyes to see my mother watching me out of one eye. When she realised I had caught her, she cleared her throat and started rubbing her eye as if she had something in it before continuing. I stifled the chuckle as I shook my head.

"Lord a t'ank yu dat yu noh mek mi daughter kill us when she tek mi fi goh get di few likkle penny di government give mi call pension an' mi few likkle Smart Price bits an' pieces a ASDA. Lord, yu know Kelly noh did even see di puss last week when she a drive. Talk 'bout di puss ina di house. Mi could see dat Lord but somebody could an' open di door an' it run out ina di road. A dat mi did a try show har. A noh mi tell har fi slam on di brakes when mi tell har fi watch di puss. A good t'ing di man behind us manage fi slam on fi him brake to. She noh did have fi vex fi dat. Di man wave at us when him pass. Mi did feel sorry fi him Lord, 'cause it look like him only have one middle finger pon di hand him did a wave. A didn't want him to feel bad soh mi just wave back wid one finger same way. A beg yu forgive mi Lord, is only afterwards Kelly tell mi what it mean. Dyam outa order buff teet bwoy!"

I opened my eyes slightly as I heard Babsie chuckling quietly. She raised her eyebrows at me and all I could do was mouthed the words,

"Don't!" as I shook my head frantically. I put my finger to my lips, pressing them tightly together to suppress the smile. Cousin Myra gave us both a stern look out of one eye.

"Sister Mala," she said quietly.

"Sorry Cousin My but him did want a lick," Mum said. Babsie collapsed on the floor, laughing. Mum opened her eyes with a puzzled look on her face. She looked from me to Babsie. Identifying the culprit, she gave Babsie 'the look'.

"Yu noh hear mi praying, Barbara? A wha' sweet yu?" she demanded. "Sorry Aunty," Babsie answered with tears rolling down her face, as she came back to a kneeling position.

"Lawd mi never see nobody can skin teet soh in all mi born days," Mum said. Babsie had long since left childhood behind but even at her age, the look from an elder could still bring her to order immediately. Cousin Myra gave us both a disapproving look but she wasn't fooling anyone. We could see she was dying to laugh too.

"Praise the Lord! T'ank you Jesus! Carry on praying for us please Sister Mala. A beg yu say a few extra words fi Babsie fi mi yu hear," she said.

"Lord, a put Kelly and Michael before you," Mum continued.

"Oh, please... not that old chestnut again," I thought.

"Lord a sorry when Sis Moore ask mi last week how many years Kelly an Michael married. Mi tongue slip when mi say 'long time'. Mi really did mean fi say *dem still noh married yet* but Satan jump pon mi tongue an' di lie just fly out.

Lord a put before yu dat likkle useless bwoy Cousin Myra hard ears gal, Tootsie, a run up an' down wid an' a mek poor Myra a bawl a night time. Rebuke him Lord an' mek him goh get a job an' stop walk up an' down a day time wid him trousers a drop off when him should an' gaan a college. A beg yu Lord when Tootsie a run up an down a night time ina dem belt deh weh she call skirt, yu clap har pon har long leg dem or cunk har in a head mek har goh home.

A put my broddah, Al, in front of yu Lord because yu know him noh have no sense from him born but it break mi heart fi see him so worried 'bout losing him job cause a di recession. Lord yu know seh him already tek pay cut an' all last week when him did sick wid flu, him still gaan a work cos poor Bliss soh worried 'bout her nursing job to since she have fi do all dat studying now fi keep up and."

At this point Cousin Myra cleared her throat, loudly, not that everything Mum was saying wasn't true, but just to remind her that we were still there and bring her back on track. My mother opened one eye again and looked at us all as I shifted the weight from one painful knee to the other.

"Lord I put Pastor Smilie an' him family in front of yu an' ask yu to bless dem. I also put the rest of my family in front of you, young an' old, good an' bad. None of us is perfect but wi trying. We've had a good year as a family and some nice times together even though we don't always see eye to eye. This year you've called a few home and you've given us some new additions. Wi not rich people Lord but wi all have food to eat an' we all have a roof over our head and that's more than a lot of people in this world so in all things we t'ank you Lord 'cause everyt'ing is everyt'ing. Amen."

"Amen" we all echoed.

"Hallelujah!" Cousin My added. "Praise the Lord!"

We hugged each other. Mum planted a noisy kiss on my cheek as she hugged me.

"See yu next week same time fi goh do mi shopping," she said. As we put our coats on she gave each of us a little parcel. Mine contained a carton of apple juice and some beans from her garden – a likkle somet'ing to tek home.

We eyed the thickening snow warily and wrapped up in hats, scarves and gloves against the biting cold before leaving for our respective homes feeling blessed by our worship and the time we had spent together as a family.

12 Bad Man

"Tell mi wha' yu want, Mummy – anyt'ing… it's yours. Yu house finish pay fah yet? You want to goh on a holiday – a cruise? You'd like dat. A pay fi my maddah fi goh on a cruise once an she did love it. Or a tell yu what… what kind a cyaar yu drive? Yu want a new cyaar?"

I smiled in disbelief as I looked at the handsome, wiry, dark skinned young man in front of me who searched my face eagerly for an answer. He was actually serious! His eyes still red from crying with a little tell-tale sign of wetness on his long lashes, had seen things that I knew I would never see if I lived three life times. They had the depth of the eyes of a weary old soldier.

"I don't *want* anything," I answered, gently hoping I wouldn't offend him. "I can't take anything from you even if I wanted to," I added as his eyes narrowed slightly with suspicion as if he couldn't believe his ears or he thought I must be playing some kind of trick on him. Then his cheeks creased into dimples as the broad lop-sided grin which I'd come to know over the few weeks I had known him displayed sparkling white teeth. One front tooth with its gold cap shone as it caught the light.

"Yeah… yeah… you said that already. I understand. Cool… cool… sorry."

I reminded him that as we were a charity and always struggling for funds, he could make a small donation to us – whatever he could comfortably afford.

"Yeah, I'll do that." The young man straightened the collar of my green Next sweatshirt which was about three sizes too big for him as he stood self-consciously in front of me. His slender brown fingers were crowded with sovereigns and assorted gold rings.

"A bit too big eh Mummy but dat cool. Yu got good taste, man."

I held out his smart, designer soft leather and suede jacket. He shook his head and told me to keep it in exchange for my sweatshirt or give it to one of the youths in the project.

As he had got up to leave the counselling room, he had looked at me thoughtfully after very slightly pulling back the vertical blinds at the window and looking up and down the street.

"Yu have on anyt'ing under da sweat shirt deh, Mummy?" he had asked.

I had cocked my head to one side with raised enquiring eyebrows which I hoped conveyed the question, *"Do you want a slap?"* I was old enough to be his mother and some and about six inches taller and broader than him to boot. He had looked at me with an amused, slightly embarrassed grin.

"No, no man. A just want to borrow yu shirt an' yu cyaan tek it off if yu noh have nut'n under it."

I relaxed and opened my mouth to ask why he wanted my sweatshirt but decided not to ask. I just prayed I wouldn't see it featured on the TV later on Crime Watch.

John Smith didn't have his usual bag with him today. While I sat staring at him bemused, he had quickly taken off his jacket, revealing a Ben Sherman t-shirt. He pulled a woollen hat from his pocket and removing his baseball cap, stuffed it into his jeans pocket. He then pulled the woollen hat down over his clean shaven head.

"Yu never know when man a watch yu," he said seriously, in explanation. "Babylon dem have dem CCTV camera every weh yu turn."

"See you same time next week?" I asked. He nodded but the momentary flicker of his eyes told me his business here was done and he would not be back.

"Take care, okay?" I said.

He opened the front door and hesitated for a moment as if he wanted to say something but thought better of it.

"T'anks, Mummy... for everyt'ing, yu hear." He pressed a piece of paper into my hand. "If you ever want anyt'ing, di man on di end a dis number wi know weh fi find mi, seen." The door creaked on its rusty hinges and like a flitting shadow, John Smith was gone.

I had qualified as a counsellor several years earlier and had worked at the *"B All U Can B"* community project in various roles from admin to one-to-one counsellor, group therapist and trainer, mainly as a volunteer because as a struggling project in a deprived area of Manchester, most of the time, we had no money to pay the bills, let alone pay staff.

The project had been set up ten years earlier by someone in the community who, as a young man, had badly needed someone to talk to. He had looked around and found nothing for black people and the black family. He had trained as a counsellor and started the project as a simple support group for black men. The need had been so great that the idea had taken off and rapidly expanded with a women's group and groups for young people being set up. The project had expanded with donations from volunteers and local service users, providing free one-to-one counselling and training counsellors from the black community.

I cast my mind back to the young man's first appointment. I had looked at the name on the referral form – John Smith, no fixed abode, no contact details. The admin officer had suggested I go and make myself a cup of coffee while she found me another client because she was sure he wouldn't show up. The bell had rung at exactly 11.00am. After looking warily up and down the street, the young man had sauntered in with attitude, sporting dark shades even though it was raining outside. He had grunted a reply as to whether he was John Smith and had scrawled an illegible signature in the register and followed me into the counselling room. His walk was like a dance, swaying from side to side, silent and catlike in trainers as if ready to spring into action.

John Smith had a problem with doors being closed and being in enclosed spaces, although he didn't admit to this. We had been allocated one of the smaller counselling rooms initially with a small window that you had to stand to look out of. As I closed the door to the room, John Smith spun round as if he was a coiled spring with a look of sheer terror in his eyes.

"Are you okay?" I asked. He was obviously embarrassed by his reaction and laughed, pointing out how small the window was and asking if we could leave the door open. I explained that for confidentiality it wouldn't be a good idea as people were passing in the outside corridor. John Smith couldn't settle so I got us a larger room with a much bigger window. He was happier but every time a door closed in any part of the building, he flinched and I noticed a nervous tick at the side of his face.

Over the four weeks he attended his hour long appointments, we got used to his trademark pulled up collar, pulled down baseball cap and shades. He usually carried a spare jumper and hat in his bag which he changed into before leaving the building. He even pulled another bag out of his bag and swapped those around too.

He talked about his childhood, most of which he had spent in the Foster Care System. He had lived with twenty different foster carers by the time he was ten years old. He had vague memories of his father being abusive to his mother before being sent to prison for armed robbery. He told me of his fifteen siblings for almost as many baby mothers that he had met over the years. Then he pulled a photo out of his wallet and showed me a mixed race girl who looked about sixteen with a chubby smiling baby on her knees. He had planned to marry her, he said, but the last time he'd been sent to prison, her parents had paid for her and the baby to go and live with an aunt in Australia.

He had avoided talking about his mother except for our final session. His mother had committed suicide after having a nervous breakdown. She had been rehoused locally under the Care In The Community system and had stopped taking her medication but no-one had noticed. He had been in prison at the time. It was after telling me this that he had broken down and cried. I sat allowing him to cry, feeling helpless as if I was sticking a flimsy plaster over a septic knife wound. Throwing the wad of soggy tissues into the rubbish bin angrily, John Smith had sniffed, wiped his nose and looked up at me with the flashing smile, attempting to mask the pain in his red eyes that could only be seen if you really looked. It was my job to really look but most of the time I didn't like what I saw.

When I asked him what had made him come for counselling, he had sighed heavily and said he was tired... just tired. I asked what exactly he was tired of and he said,

"Everything... life... I don't know."

Then he had picked up the leaflet on the table about the youth project.

"Good this – mi little brother comes to it."

"Really... what's his name?"

He had smiled without answering. He didn't need to for the young man with the carbon copy dimples immediately came to mind.

"He's a good kid. He's been going to school since he started coming here. His foster carers were going to kick him out but they've decided to give him another chance. They're nice people. I've told him I'll slap him round the head if he messes up."

I smiled. "That's what we're here for... to give people another chance." He folded the leaflet and put it into his pocket.

"I've got a sister," he said. "I'm going to give this to her."

"Good. Would you like to talk about some of the things you are tired of?" I asked. He shook his head.

"It's too much to tell... maybe next time."

About a week after my last counselling session with John Smith, the admin officer came into the *B All U Can B Project* to find a wad of rolled up £20 notes, totalling £500 in the letter box with the mail. It had the specific instructions that it was to be used for the Youth Counselling Group. I'd like to think it was from John Smith. The Project manager after getting advice from the local police, said as it had been donated anonymously and we had no way of knowing if it had been earned from illegal activities, we could pay it into the Project's bank account.

The donation paid for a trip to the Liverpool Slavery Museum which the young people had asked to go to and a meal afterwards in a restaurant. Most of the young people had never been outside Manchester and only one of them had ever eaten in a restaurant. We toasted our anonymous benefactor in Coke and lemonade.

John Smith talked about wanting to be a pilot as a child. His mother, before she had become ill, had given him a photograph of her grandfather who had been a pilot in the Royal Air Force during the Second World War. John Smith showed me the picture of a young man who looked exactly like him in RAF uniform, holding his cap under his arm. He kept the photograph in his wallet next to the picture of his ex-girlfriend and baby.

The young man told me that after seeing that photograph of his great grandfather, he too had wanted to be a pilot. His teacher had laughed and told him not to be so stupid because boys like him couldn't be pilots. She added that she would definitely not board any aeroplane piloted by him. She had given him a football and told him to go and play outside because she wanted to drink her tea in peace. He told me that was the day he had first met the big lads from the estate with the tablets in an envelope. They had been hanging about on the other side of the school fence, smoking weed.

The first time he had been sent to prison for selling drugs it had been to get enough money to take his mother to see a private doctor because he had felt the medication her G.P. had prescribed for her was actually causing her depression instead of curing it. While in prison he had decided that he would prove his primary school teacher wrong. He had first studied for his GCSEs, then his 'A' levels during another sentence. During his last spell in prison, he had got a First Class Honours Degree in Civil Engineering but he had still been unable to get a job on his release.

"I've done all of dem stupid dead end government training schemes," he said. "I got fed up working just fi mi dole money and a tenner. What's £10 to a big man?" he asked kissing his teeth. "The only scheme I ever liked was the one run by some of the local ministers and youth workers. They had a thing called The Churches Work Scheme where they taught us how to make and upholster furniture. That was the only one that ever taught me a real skill and treated us with respect but I think they close down because they couldn't get any funding so I ended up back inside."

As I stood in the newsagents and looked at the photograph of the serious dark skinned young man, a gasp escaped my lips as the memories came flooding back. For years I had wondered what had become of the young man I had counselled. He looked younger in the picture than I remembered but it was unmistakably John Smith. Confidentiality had prevented me from making any enquiries from people who might have known him. The last I heard his brother had got a place at Manchester University. The teenager whom I assumed was his sister still attends the Youth Group at the *B All U can B Project*.

A cold chill ran down my spine.

"Did you know him?" The newsagent asked.

"Er... not really. I just met him a few times."

"These kids eh. We never had it this easy in my days. They have everything laid out on a plate for them and they just waste it. They all think they're bad men carrying their guns and their knives," he continued but I wasn't listening as I picked up the paper and read the head-lines: "Local Gang leader Shot Dead."

"What a waste of a young life. Do you want that paper, love?"

I went home and with tears in my eyes searched in the pocket of my old handbag for the piece of paper John Smith had given to me with the number of the person he said could reach him anytime. The least I could do was to attend his funeral and put some flowers on his grave.

13 Browning

My extended family between us have our finger on the pulse when it comes to current events and trends. It was, therefore, no surprise to me when we met at my Cousin Myra's house New Year's Day for dinner and the topic of skin bleaching came up.

The older heads in particular, have their own unique take on everything that obviously makes perfect sense to them but often not to anyone else. To be honest, I think sometimes my family know that what they are saying makes no sense but they continue the story for the hell of it and for our amusement, especially, as on this occasion, after they have had a drink or two.

As we ate, we debated the question which my brother John Joseph (JJ) had raised on another occasion, of whether society was informed by the media and fed off it or the other way around. My little brother wasn't nicked named 'The Professor' for nothing so it was quite a tough topic to chew over with the rice 'n' peas. As usual, family members vied with each other to express their particular opinion.

We all agreed that in recent years newspaper headlines had become increasingly dominated by stories of the outrageous behaviour of stars who appear not to be good role models for our youth who idolise them.

My eldest daughter, Shari, commented that the behaviour of certain stars in all genres seemed to be dictated by their need to grab and keep the spot light on themselves due to the growing competition and pressure to get to the top and stay there. JJ added that they appeared to present certain negative images deliberately to attract and generate media attention. He cited the example of the popular female singer who recently felt it was okay to go on stage and perform dressed in raw meat. The shocked silence and looks of horror all round said it all I think.

My aunt Barbara, known as Bliss, said it seemed everything 'bad' was good or if not touted as 'good' was being presented to us as acceptable.

"These days even the words 'good' and 'bad' are interchangeable. If you don't agree that good is bad and bad is good then you are seen as having a problem. The world's gone mad!" There were nods of agreement all round as family members sipped drinks and munched on peanuts and banana chips. A couple of people looked thoughtful, as if they didn't quite get it.

"Di government want us to think is poor people one a commit crime and gwaan bad but dem not fooling a soul. Look at all these people in top positions like di politician dem weh a teef people money fi how long at Westminster. Another one gaan a jail this week fi fiddling him expenses. As for dem sports people deh – dem worse! What sweet dem why dem cyaan stay wid one woman? Mi noh know why dem just noh turn Muslim and done," Mum said.

We were doing well; glasses were clinking, the peanuts had nearly all gone and no-one had fallen out so far. There were more nods and murmurs of agreement, mainly from the men, especially after Shari's husband, Omar, who is a Muslim, explained that their religion allowed them to have more than one wife. The women in my family, like most Jamaicans, are very good at conveying their thoughts with one expression. A look from Shari which clearly said, *over my dead body*, made Omar quickly add that he didn't agree with that and one wife was more than enough for him. I for one was glad to hear that. Michael just gave a little cough and looked up briefly from his CDs.

My mother continued that behaviour when she was a girl, that would have been condemned nationally and either resulted in imprisonment or confinement to a 'madhouse' as she put it, is today applauded and encouraged or smiled at indulgently and excused.

"Anyt'ing goes these days," Cousin Myra butted in."From women starving themselves into size zero clothes –"

"No chance of that in this family," Uncle Al interrupted with a chuckle, glancing at Aunty Bliss'generous curves.

" – to plastic surgeons remodelling people from head to toe soh dem can walk about in public half naked and leave nothing to the imagination," Cousin My continued, ignoring him.

"Mi like when dem noh leave nut'n to the imagination," Uncle Al blurted out. I think he forgot for a moment where he was but Aunty Bliss' cold stare quickly reminded him.

"Er... yu right Myra... damn disgrace!" he added clearing his throat and turning to my partner Michael, aka Mixer, with an almost seamless change of subject. "Er... Mixer what about music?"

"I don't play most of the modern stuff when I'm on the radio," Michael answered.

"That's because you're getting old, Dad. You're not with it anymore," Lolly said.

"Thanks for that, Lolly, but it's because I like to play music that's positive and I don't know what some of these singers are going to come out with next. Some of these modern pop and dance hall songs – Lord have mercy! " Michael said. "All those derogatory and sexually explicit lyrics, glorifying drugs and violence, and dem wonder why di likkle yoot dem killing each other."

Ferdie, my cousin Barbara's husband took a sip of his glass of sorrel. Cousin Myra had made a low sugar version of the Christmas treat just for him to compensate for him not being able to drink any alcohol due to his diabetes.

"We going round and round in circles man, so let me explain to all of you how this t'ing work," he said. Mum groaned, rolled her eyes and took a sip of her sweet sherry.

"Aww... no Uncle Ferdie," Lolly protested. "Dad, can you change that music, please!"

"Yeah Mixer." Ferdie turned to Michael. "Myra gospel music is making me depressed. Put on somet'ing wi can shake a leg to."

"I heard that!" Cousin My shouted from the kitchen. "There's nothing wrong with good gospel music!"

"Yeah – *good* gospel music! When yu in church!" Ferdie shouted back. "Hear mi now, Lolly Man," he continued. "People read 'bout t'ings in the newspaper or see it on TV and dem seh, 'kiss mi neck back! A soh it goh? Is that what everybody else doing? Mi have to do it too because mi noh want no-body t'ink seh mi not intelligent or mi old fashion. Mi have fi get one over on Mass Filbert and Miss Punsy next door.'"

"That's it exactly, Uncle Ferdie," JJ chuckled. "Mum says what I'm saying doesn't make any sense but people do things and it's reported in the paper or they make a film or TV programme about something and then people *start* to do it *because* they saw it in the media."

"So that explains where all the trouble start – the day humans learn fi read an' write," Mum said. "Hmmm! Dem better stop try fi teach monkey fi read or wi in trouble."

Just then, Tiana (Tootsie), Cousin Myra's daughter came into the room, carrying napkins for the table and nodding her head to the music.

"That's better Uncle Michael," she whispered, glancing over her shoulder. Yeah…yeah….yeah!" she sang, rolling her hips from side to side.

"Chile, stop wine up yuself an' come 'ere," Mum said. "Is wha'appen to yu skin why it look so…   fluxie fluxie and yu mout' part look soh dark? Yu sick? " My mother took hold of Tootsie's chin, lifted her head and squinted at her curiously. Tootsie obviously wasn't happy as she shifted from one leg to the other, but she didn't dare move away.

"It's just make-up, Grandma," she said quietly. Cousin Myra looked uncomfortable as she followed Tootsie into the room carrying a steaming dish of sweet potatoes with melting butter and fresh herbs. Tootsie's head rose defiantly at the look her mother gave her.

"Is true, Aunty Mala," Cousin Babsie added. "I was t'inking di same t'ing. Ferdie yu noh si how she look like that singer bwoy weh claim seh him nah bleach him skin. Tiana always a listen to him outa order song dem."

"Yeah man. That's how you can tell when dem a bleach... dem look like vampire an' dem mouth turn black like dem leave it out ina di sun too long by itself," Ferdie chuckled. "Tootsie, a hope it's not him yu a follow."

"I don't know what you all mean. I'm not bleaching my skin," Tootsie answered, scowling at Babsie and Ferdie.

"If yu stop tell lie it pay yu better," Cousin My said as she came in again. She kissed her teeth as she slammed the dish of fried plantain she was carrying onto the table, making everyone jump. Aunty Bliss caught My's other hand just in time and taking the jug of Guinness punch which she was holding out of it, placed it carefully onto the table.

"A bleaching cream she a use yu hear Sister Mala. For weeks now she a deny it but mi find it ina har room last week."

"I told you it wasn't mine, Mum!" Tootsie cried defensively, wheeling round to glare at her mother.

"Bleaching cream? Bleaching cream weh yu use fi clean bathroom?"

"No, Grandma, I'm not stupid!" Tootsie shouted. The whole room went quiet as my mother's mouth tightened at the corners.

"What a friend we have in Jesus..." she began to hum as she slowly walked back over to where Tootsie was standing. She pulled herself up to her full height and standing in front of Tootsie, placed her hands on her hips.

"Is who yu talking to?" she asked in that voice which we all knew meant, *be very careful how you answer this question if you want to have teeth to brush tomorrow morning.*

"Chile, mi look like yu maddah to yu?" Tootsie, like the rest of us, obviously couldn't see the likeness so, to all our relief, she wisely assessed her situation, recognised the position of the alpha female and backed down.

"No, Grandma... sorry."

"Aho!" Mum said and walked back to her chair, humming, *"... all our sins and grief to bear."*

"It's a special kind of cream that some people are using to lighten their skin, Grandma," Lolly answered.

"They even have tablets and injections that lighten your skin now," JJ added.

"Er... There are some Nigerian girls at uni who bleach all the time but Tootsie's skin doesn't look like that," Lolly said, I think in an attempt to help Tootsie out.

"Lighten yu skin? How dat work? What... sun tan in reverse?" Mum asked, baffled.

"I wasn't trying to lighten my skin," Tootsie said, quietly this time, between clenched teeth.

"It's a big multi-million dollar business right up there with black hair products, Mum. Somebody is making big money out of black people and it isn't us," JJ said.

"Lord, what's wrong with people een? Half di world t'ink dem too white and paying good money fi bun up dem skin ina sun, now di other half t'ink dem too black an' paying a fortune buying cream fi turn white?"

"Who decides what's too black or too white anyway?" Aunty Bliss asked

"A noh jus' black people you know. A lot of people from India and Pakistan and dem place deh use bleaching creams too. I was watching a documentary about it. There's been a big increase in skin problems because of it."

"But Lord, yu really are a very fair God. Look how yu mek fool fool people ina every race and colour een?" Mum said.

"Your mother certainly has a way with words," Michael whispered with a smile.

"Hmmm.... is cause some people love fi jump ina everything an' faas with black people somet'ing an' call demself black when it suit dem but dem noh want no-body call dem black," Uncle Al said.

"And just as many black and mixed race people doing things because they want to be white or light skinned, Uncle Al," my daughter Shari said.

"But Indian and Pakistani people and such are not black," Mum said.

"You know we all get lumped in together, Grandma. Some Asians have darker skin than some West Indians though," Shari answered. "With the ones who are using bleaching products, I think it's because of their social caste system. The darker you are the lower your caste. Dark skinned people who are usually the ones who work out in the fields are outside the caste system all together. They call them untouchables so no-one wants to be dark skinned."

"Just like in slavery days, the light skinned or mulatto slave dem did t'ink dem better than the dark ones dem weh work ina di fields just cause dem work ina house," Uncle Al said." That's why dem love di browning dem soh much in Jamaica."

"A di first mi hear 'bout this Caste system? Yu mean like upper class and middle class people?"

"Mmmm," Shari answered.

"I wonder what dem must tink 'bout us real black people?" Mum asked. "Yu right yu know Al. From wi growing up in Jamaica, some people t'ink if you have brown skin and have tall hair yu better than somebody with dark skin an' dry head but why dem feel dem can use bleach pon dem skin?"

"Some black people are too obsessed with light skin," JJ said. It's all about status and fitting in. Why do you think most of these stars marry white people?"

I thought back to when I lived in Jamaica and got into many arguments on my cousin Babsie's behalf because other children used to tease her about her dark skin but we knew those children were only repeating what they had heard from their parents. Babsie was obviously thinking along the same lines.

"You wouldn't understand yu hear JJ," Babsie said with a sigh.

"Sometimes it's not about you not liking the way *you* are, it's about *other people* not liking you the way you are. Kelly, do you remember Vincent and Sandra? Sandra maddah was a teacher at Black Hill School and har father was head deacon in the church. Sandra was light skin – original browning. She met and brought Vincent into the church. He was a really nice bwoy and everybody could see dat dem love each other but har parents wouldn't let har marry him because dem seh him too dark. Vincent left the church and never came back. I was only young but I can still remember it because Vincent and I were the same complexion."

Hearing the pain in Babsie's voice, Ferdie kissed his teeth.

"Dem crazy! Browning? Mi only have eyes for my original black empress straight from outa di African sun, noh true, baby," he said wrapping his arms around Babsie. Babsie's head went up as she smiled smugly and snuggled close to her husband.

"Well yu noh know wha' dem seh Ferdie?" Uncle Al asked.

"No, what?"

"Di darker di berry, di sweeter di juice, bwoy. Ha! Ha! Ha!"

"Yu know it! Put it there bwoy!"

Uncle Al and Ferdie exchanged a high five.

"I don't know why people just never satisfied with what dem get, whether it's skin, hair or body" Cousin Myra said, placing a piece of chicken on Uncle Al's plate. Uncle Al looked from his plate to Ferdie's as Cousin My put a bigger piece on his plate.

"Maybe cause dem get short changed. Dem get less than di man next to dem and dem noh happy. Dem want more a di good t'ings in life." He winked at me. I smiled as his complaint went completely over Cousin My's head and she just continue serving. Ferdie smirked and Uncle Al made a stab for his chicken but Ferdie deftly moved his plate out of the way and Uncle Al stabbed the table with his fork. Mum eyed them both disapprovingly from across the table.

"Wha'appen to di two a yu?" she asked.

"Nut'n" they both answered in unison.

"Noh one facey fly a try pitch pon Ferdie meat," Uncle Al added.

"Where yu see fly in di middle a winter?" Mum asked, helping herself to spoonfuls of rice n peas.

"Poor wi. We just lost sheep wid out a shepherd," Cousin My said sadly.

"The media is our shepherd so we'll forever want," JJ chuckled.

"It isn't funny John Joseph. Di pop star dem turn people God," Mum said.

"Or footballers," Uncle Al added. "They're just as bad. I want to be a football player and get some a all dat money and all dem nice girls deh." Aunty Bliss looked at him and kissed her teeth. "Yes, yu gwaan goh turn football player wid yu flat foot dem, yu hear," she said. "As long as yu bring me all di money yu can keep di likle fluxie gal dem."

"Well if Christians follow Christ is only natural that people are gonna copy whoever they worship. Yu t'ink is mistake why dem call dem idol? Di idol dem just have a different face nowadays. Dem noh mek outa gold, dem just mek gold, noh true Cousin My?" Ferdie said.

Much as it pained Cousin Myra, she nodded her agreement and added that the Bible said man was made to worship, so if they didn't worship God then they had to worship something.

"Well listen noh. Unnuh hear what the singer bwoy deh weh Tootsie a listen to, seh mek him skin gone pale?"

"He said he uses cake soap, Uncle," Shari said.

"Now, let me explain it to all a yu di way I see it," Uncle Al said.

"Explain what?" Aunty Bliss asked on all our behalf.

"Well," Uncle Al said pushing his chair back from the table. "Yu know how di Bible seh God mek us outa dust an' dem seh is Africa wi all come from originally?"

"Yes..." Aunty Bliss answered, slowly as we all looked at each other.

"But scientist cyaan figure out how white people change from dust colour which is brown. Noh true? Dark brown, light brown maybe, but still brown, yeah, to... white."

"Yes..." Aunty Bliss said again, cautiously. Knowing Uncle Al well, we perked up our ears and continued to look at him expectantly. Some of us were already smiling.

"Well, it must be cake soap dem did a use from dem days deh when dem come off Noah's Ark." JJ and Ferdie started to chuckle.

"Al, what kind a foolishness yu talking now?" Cousin Myra asked.

"Listen noh man, you know the story better than the rest of us Myra. Noah had three sons, Shem, Ham and Japheth. I'm going to tell you how we get white people from black people. Everybody start off black... well brown but you know dem call everyone weh have any likkle colour black these days. Mrs Noah must have cooked up a boss batch a cake soap after the family come off the Ark. She noh did have nut'n fi do cause she noh have di whole heap a animal dem fi feed noh more. Yu noh see it? That's why Shem and Japheth and dem family colour fade to white. But look 'ere noh, no-body noh let poor Ham in on di secret 'cause dem did already fall out wid him after Noah run him and him son Canaan outa di yard because if you remember, Ham laugh after Noah when him get drunk and fall asleep naked in him tent. When Noah wake up, Shem and Japheth grass up Ham. Noh true, Cousin My?"

Myra nodded hesitantly, not too sure where the story was going. Uncle Al realising he had our complete attention, took a sip from his glass.

"But I don't think that was fair, especially for Canaan, Noah grandson, because him get curse and him noh do nut'n. Poor Ham couldn't help being disrespectful 'cause him a the middle son and a soh middle pickney give trouble. So, this is how Ham came to be black people ancestor. After Noah run him outa di yard, Ham goh wonder ina di hot desert sun and bake likkle. God did have to turn up the temperature a bit to dry up all the flood water. Meanwhile Ham a bake ina di desert and a bawl 'bout how life unfair, guess what? The rest a di family dem back a yard a use cake soap an' a turn white."

My brother JJ was the first to go. He collapsed in fits of laughter followed by the rest of us. Uncle Al just sat with the mischievous satisfied smirk that made him look so much like my mother.

"What?" he asked innocently. "A same soh it happen. Yu noh see it? Dem a give scientist millions of pounds fi carry out research and figure out why some a wi white and some black when we all descended from Adam an' Eve, an' mi just work it out fi dem."

Aunty Bliss wiped tears of laughter from her eyes as she shook her head. "Al..." was all she said.

"Noh drink noh more brandy, Al," Mum said.

"Sister Mala, where yu get this brother from?" Cousin Myra asked, still chuckling. "Bliss is how yu live wid him soh long?"

Uncle Al too was laughing now. "Unnuh just jealous 'cause mi too clever fi unnuh. You see how unnuh stay," he said. "Unnuh soon read that ina story book. Bet if a white man did tell yu dat, yu would an' believe and run goh tell everybody but because is me poor likkle black man and Vybz Kartel tell unnuh what cake soap can do, unnuh noh believe. Cho! Dat's why other people teef all wi invention dem an' seh is dem invent it when a black man but noh body noh did believe dem." Uncle Al kissed his teeth. "Poor singer bwoy... mi know what it feel like when no-body noh believe yu. Bet when him turn white good good 'til him have fi goh get sun tan, unnuh wi believe seh a cake soap do it. Vybz mi son, when dem come to yu fi borrow yu soap, yu waan just run dem from yu."

"So, Al, tell mi somet'ing, how come my old granmaddah a wash har white clothes wid cake soap from mi a yoot an' har hand dem noh turn white yet?" Ferdie asked.

"Is cause yu granmaddah hand dem mek outa iron. Yu remember di lick dem she used to give us. Kiss mi neckback! See stars? Mi see blinkie, titiboo, firefly, anyt'ing yu waan call dem. Mi see dem a fly round mi head," Uncle Al answered as he and Ferdie burst out laughing.

"The two of you eat your dinner an' stop talking foolishness now," Mum said.

I happened to glance at Tootsie next to me who didn't seem to be enjoying the merriment.

"What happened with the bleaching cream?" I asked quietly.

"Aunty Kay don't you start as well. Nothing!"

"No, don't get angry, just tell me."

"I wasn't trying to bleach my skin... honest. Well I was sort of... but not my skin... er... just my spots but Mum just jumped to conclusions and wouldn't listen to me."

I nodded for her to continue.

"It was my friend's cream. I just borrowed it to put a bit on a couple of scars on my chin where I had spots to make them fade. I don't want to change colour. I like the colour I am."

"I'm glad to hear that. Your chin doesn't look that bad. Did it work?"

"No. I only put it on a couple of times but it gave me a rash and made my chin sore."

"So you won't be using it again?

"No, I threw it in the bin. That's where Mum found it. I'm not using that rubbish on my skin again."

"So why does your face look like that?"

"It's a new foundation one of my friends gave me as a present, Aunty Kay. She's white and I don't think she really understands about different skin colour. I think it's just too light for me but I didn't want to hurt her feelings. I'm gonna buy a darker one next week."

"So why didn't you tell your mum that."

"Because she never listens to me and Grandma is just as bad."

"Shall I explain to them later?"

Tootsie nodded with a relieved smile. "Mum will listen to you and then she might believe me."

"Okay, just leave your skin alone and let nature take its course but if you're really desperate to get rid of your acne scars and even out your complexion," I said. "Try cake soap."

"What is cake soap anyway?" Tootsie asked.

"It's household general purpose soap that people use in Jamaica."

"Ordinary soap can't bleach your skin no matter how strong it is," Tootsie laughed. " Can it?"

"Ah... Tootsie my love, there is the million dollar question. You'd better ask Vibz Kartel next time you see him," I said.

14 Through The Eyes of A Child

This is a cautionary tale for parents or anyone who associates with snmall children. If you didn't know this already, beware of what you say and do in front of your mini acquaintances because in their innocence they will bury you with the stark truth of the world as they see and make sense of it. You will die laughing or of embarrassment every time they open their mouths.

Small children, I have discovered, have a natural ability to think outside of the box because they have not yet been influenced by adult's prejudices and don't know the complex rules by which we live and make our lives far more confusing than is necessary. Because you children are telling the truth or regurgitating what they hear from our own lips, one cannot in all honesty reprimand them. If you do, it will only backfire on you because today's children are not as they used to be and, outraged, they will defend themselves, the loudly and embarrass you even more. Does this ring a bell? *"But Mummy (insert whatever name you care to here) you did say that Aunty Janey's* bottom looks like an elephant walking away."

At best, cringing with embarrassment, you can stuff a sweet into the child's mouth and quickly take them out of the room or you can whisper *"shut up!"* through clenched teeth or out of the side of your mouth. All this while smiling sweetly at their audience who like gleeful voyeurs are eager to lap up the juicy titbits of indiscreet revelations.

"Nanny has that man got a baby in his tummy?" my lovely grandson loudly asked recently when an overweight man got into the packed life we were in. The teenage boys at the back of the lift covered their faces and sniggered while my grandson, Issy, looked innocently up at us all.

The other people in the life looked resolutely straight ahead. To their credit, it must have taken Herculean effort not to laugh too.

"No baby in here, son," the man said good-naturedly patting his protruding stomach, "just too much dinner and beer."

"Too much dinner? Are you too greedy?" Issy asked seriously. I apologised profusely to the man who just smiled graciously. As my grandson opened his mouth to say something else, I rushed the little darling out of the lift two floors before ours, praying that I would never see that man again.

On another occasion, my cousin Myra, who was visiting, and I were enjoying a joke when Issy wondered into the room. He looked from me to Cousin My with an exaggerated smile: the one that's all teeth and scrunched up eyes that small children do, when they are not quite sure what's going on but would like to get in on the act.

"Nanny, are you not fed up of Cousin My and her bible bashing today?" he asked. I swallowed hard and experienced one of those moments where it feels like time stands still as I thought, *"Oh Lord, he didn't just say that!"* My face burned with embarrassment and had I been white, I would have been a lovely shade of beetroot.

"Hmm... bible bashing?" Cousin Myra asked sternly after Issy had left the room, no doubt to innocently created mischief elsewhere.

"Er... no, no not at all Cousin My... I er... always enjoy our bible discussions," I lied. "I don't know where Issy got that from."

I believe Issy thought for a while that everyone has two mothers and fathers because his parents and my partner Michael and I refer to each other's parents as 'mum' and 'dad'. This is genealogy of our complex extended family as explained by my grandson, aged almost four, that had us all bent double in fits of laughter.

My cousin Barbara, known to us as Babsie, was obviously feeling bored and mischievous, I think, at a recent family gathering.

"Kelly, yu t'ink Issy ever get confuse wid all di different pet names and such we call our one another? Yu know what a mean? Like how wi call everybody aunty, uncle, cousin whether wi related by blood or marriage."

"I don't think so," I answered. "Why don't you ask him?" Having had some thought provoking conversations with the young man in question I thought, *hmm... this should be good.*

"Issy," Babsie asked, "where is your grandma?" My grandson looked puzzled.

"She's there," he replied, pointing to my mother.

"No, this is grandma," Babsie said, pointing to me.

"No, that's my Nanny," Issy answered.

"How do you know *that* is Nanny?" Babsie asked. Issy looked at me, then at Cousin Babsie with a look that clearly said, *I think this woman has lost it.*

"Because, when I was a baby my mummy – this one," he added, pointing to my daughter, Shari, to emphasise his point, "told me."

"Oh... but this is Kelly," Babsie continued, pointing to me.

"Yes... I know," Issy answered patiently, "but Nanny said I'm not allowed to call her that until I'm at least a hundred."

"Oh, I see," Babsie answered, trying hard to keep a straight face. "You've got a little while to go then... before you get to a hundred?"

"Yes, five sleeps... I think."

"So Issy, this is Nanny and that is Grandma, is that right?" Babsie asked.

"Yes," Issy answered slowly with a nod.

"And this is Granddad," Babsie said pointing to my partner, Michael, "so he must live with Grandma, yes?" Issy rolled on the floor laughing, holding his face in his hands.

"No... that's Granddad Michael! He belongs to Nanny!"

"Really? I thought he was called Mixer," Babsie said referring to Michael's nickname.

"Yes, he's called Granddad Michael *and* Mixer but Nanny calls him 'baby' when he's a good boy."

"Is that right?" So what does Nanny call you when you're a good boy?"

"She calls me baby too but we're not really babies. Nanny just calls us that because she likes us."

"So if Granddad Michael doesn't live with Grandma, who lives with her and looks after her?" Babsie asked.

"Jesus," came the answer instantly. "Grandma doesn't have a man at her house. She said they give too much talking."

"Too much talking eh? I think she might be right there," Cousin Babsie said looking over at her husband, Ferdie.

"What?" Ferdie asked.

"Yes, my grandma's always right. She did have a granddad when she wasn't old; I've seen his picture in his hat and his big suit when they didn't have any colours in that world."

Babsie looked at me, puzzled.

"He means a black and white photograph," I said in explanation. There was a chorus of "Oh..." around the room as understanding dawned.

"Grandma's granddad lives in the *cementary* now,"Issy said. Babsie looked at me again for an explanation.

"Cemetery," I said.

By now all conversation in the room had ceased and everyone was listening and trying hard not to laugh out loud.

"He got sick and Grandma has to take him lots of flowers to make him better," Issy added. "Grandma said Grandpa John is resting 'til Jesus comes. I think Grandpa John likes flowers."

"Why do you think that?" Babsie asked.

"He had a lot of flowers on his house in the cementary. Nanny took me to visit him but I didn't see him though. I don't think he was in." Several people had to hurriedly leave the room at this point and the sound of loud laughter could be heard coming from the hall.

"Issy," Babsie asked, "what about Cousin Myra? Who does she live with?"

"Cousin My lives with her girl, Tiana."

"Oh you mean Tootsie."

"Yes, but I think Jesus lives at their house too, sometimes when he's not at Grandma's because Cousin My said, Jesus is her husband and he takes care of her."

"So what about your Uncle JJ; who are his family?"

"He belongs to Aunty Julie and their girl and their big boys. Cousin Babsie, did you know that Nanny used to be Grandma's baby but she got too big for the pram so she had to buy a car?"

"Er... no, I didn't know that. So, Issy what is your daddy's mummy called?" *Hello... I thought. We're going into another realm altogether now. This should be interesting.*

"Daddy calls her mbamaa in his words but I just call her mamaa."

Cousin Babsie looked at Shari's husband, Omar, with enquiring raised eyebrows.

"That's right," Omar said. "It's almost the same in Mandinka as in English."

"Did you know Cousin Babsie that my daddy used to belong to somewhere else called Gambia? You have to go on an aeroplane up in the sky a long, long way."

"Is that right?"

"Yes, but Daddy belongs to me and Mummy now. Don't you Dad?"

"Yes, that's right, son," Omar answered.

"That's why Daddy knows lots of different words for things. I know some of my daddy's words too 'cos Daddy said I need to learn them so that I can talk to *Mamaa* when she phones from Gambia."

"You're a good boy," Cousin Babsie said.

"I know," Issy answered. "Daddy thinks I am too and he gives me sweeties when I learn more of his words. He says I'm a very clever boy."

"And your daddy is right. Thank you for helping me to understand," Cousin Babsie said. My grandson had a beaming smile on his face.

"That's all right," he said. "Do you want to know anything else? I will help you if you don't know a lot of things."

"Omar has been teaching him to speak Mandinka – one of his languages," Shari said in explanation.

"One a yu language, Omar?" Ferdie asked. "Is how many language yu speak, blood?"

"I speak five languages fluently," Omar replied. "Mandinka and Wallof, our two main languages, but also English of course, Dutch and German."

"Backfoot! Gwaan my yoot!" my uncle Al cried, slapping Omar on his back. "An' all dis time mi a cuss yu seh yu cyaan talk." Omar just laughed.

"That's nothing unusual for Gambians you know Uncle Al," I said. "in fact England is one of the few countries where people don't speak another language or two fluently. That's why I've been encouraging Omar to teach Issy Mandinka."

"There are at least ten languages spoken in Gambia apart from English because of the different tribes," Omar said. "*Radio Gambia* broadcasts its news in five different languages."

"Ah soh? Mi noh did know dat," Babsie said.

"Yes a true! Everywhere yu goh on holiday no matter what dem language, dem speak English these days. An' yu cyaan even speak the one language yu know properly eh Babsie?" my uncle Al teased.

"Al, noh baddah start yu know. A two language mi speak, wha'ppen to yu?" Babsie replied kissing her teeth.

"How yu work dat one out?" Uncle Al asked.

"A two language all a wi speak, Al. English and patois."

"Patois a noh real language," Ferdie said. "A just mek wi mek it up."

"A soh yu t'ink," Babsie replied. "Cousin My a noh yu tell mi seh dem a write patois bible now?"

"Yes, mi check it out after Ferdie seh him wi only read di bible of it in patois an' guess what Ferdie?"

"No man, mi noh believe dat. Nut'n noh goh soh," Ferdie said, shaking his head.

"Strange as it might sound, Ferdie, it's true," I said. "I read somewhere about a Jamaican minister, Reverend Courtney... somebody..."

"Stewart," my brother JJ said. "His name is Reverend Courtney Stewart and he is the General Secretary of the Bible Society of the West Indies. They're spending £250,000 on a project to translate the bible into patois."

"But Lord... what is dis?" my mother said. "Bongo talk really a noh disgrace noh more fi true."

"Big t'ings really a gwaan wid fi wi likkle bongo talk as Mala call it," Uncle Al said.

"Mi dear sah!" Babsie said. "Yu noh see it. An' fi show yu seh a real language, yu goh outside goh find a English person and speak to dem ina patois and see if dem understand a word weh yu a seh. Yu noh hear mi speaking English to Issy 'cos him noh understand patois. Him maddah noh to him ina patois."

"Mi was wondering why yu talking so speakey spokey," Ferdie said. "A high time wi fi promote it and stop feel shame fi speak our maddah tongue."

"Ain't that di truth!" Babsie answered. "But when we was likkle an' growing up, my maddah used to beat us fa speaking patois and tell us fi speak English. Bwoy times change een?"

"Well all I know is, I'm going to buy the first copy of the patois bible for yu, yu hear Ferdie?" Cousin Myra said.

"Cousin Babsie," Issy said. "I'm teaching my daddy the words that you and Grandma and Aunty Bliss say because he doesn't understand."

"Issy is teaching me to speak Jamaican patois," Omar laughed.

Just then my younger sister, Clara, wondered in sipping a mug of tea and looked around, perplexed at the room's amused occupants.

"What's going on?" she asked. "What are you lot up to now?" She soon found out.

"Issy," Cousin Babsie said, with a mischievous twinkle in her eyes, "who does Aunty Clara belong to?"

"She lives with her man," came the flat reply. Looking up into the air with a thoughtful frown, he continued. "I think he's called a husband though. Grandma says he's a toy boy but he's not." Clara nearly choked on her tea and began to cough violently.

"I think he's a real boy because I've never seen his strings and his nose doesn't grow. Only Pinocchio is a toy boy isn't it Nanny?"

"Er... yes dear," I replied as I tried to keep a straight face.

My mother's face was a picture as my sister looked at her and she looked back, embarrassed, as if something was stuck in her throat. Fortunately, Clara had a sense of humour and her 'toy boy' husband had gone outside with some of the other men or, as they say, that's where the argument would have started.

"Babsie, what kind of outa order question those yu asking the child?" Mum snapped when she recovered from the shock.

"Bwoy why yu chat soh much?" she asked turning to Issy.

"That means 'be quiet' Daddy," Issy said turning to his father. The room exploded in laughter.

"Yu didn't t'ink it was outa order before yu get caught out," my Uncle Al laughed. "Hee hee hee! No baddah blame poor likkle Issy. Mala, admit it man, yu get ketch! Ketch hook, line and sinker!"

Mum kissed her teeth, while Issy sought sanctuary on his father's lap.

"Mi noh know when him learn fi chat soh much," Mum said.

That day I think we all made a mental note to be more aware of the little ones around us and what we say in front of them, if we don't want to end up in prison or start a war. We also realised that spelling words or speaking patois so the children don't understand us doesn't work anymore because times as well as children have changed since I was a child. I don't know if it's something in the food, the water or the air but "pickney born these days able to spell an' pronounce" as my mother says. Given the huge advances, technological and otherwise of recent decades, when this generation grow up and put their mark on the world, it will not be a place that anyone old enough to vote now will recognise.